Silent
WARRIOR

Silent
WARRIOR

One Woman's Triumph Over
Traumatic Brain Injury

CELIA BELT *and* BETHANY COOMES

Broer Books

First Edition

Print ISBN 978-1-7321040-2-0

eBook ISBN 978-1-7321040-3-7

DEDICATION

I dedicate this book to my late husband, Randy, my children, Justin, Jarred, Hillary, and to my loving friends. They were truly on the front lines of my recovery and had to learn to live with the after effects of my accident. I believe they all accepted and adjusted to the new me. I acknowledge that this was not an easy road for them.

I also dedicate this book to the expert team of doctors, therapists and clinicians who helped me rebuild a life that I considered shattered and quite imperfect. I could not have reached the best possible health outcomes without these committed individuals. I'll never be the same; yet, I am now the best version of myself due to their remarkable work.

Lastly, this book is dedicated to you, the reader who is seeking his or her own form of normalcy, whether you have suffered a traumatic event yourself or are a loved one attempting to cope with and adjust to someone else's injury. It's a long road, but I assure you that you can step back and watch the progress if your loved one gets the correct clinical support.

Never give up and don't give in. Society may label you, but I suggest you choose your own label. As I chose mine...The Silent Warrior....

TABLE OF CONTENTS

PREFACE

Broer and I go Medieval

This book is written for all those who have experienced a traumatic brain injury or any traumatic event in their life and for those who have loved ones who have experienced a traumatic injury. These wounds can be complex. They can be mild in nature or quite brutal. I have found through my work with burn and blast survivors that many do not even know they have a TBI until years after the accident. They have lived with the debilitating and confusing symptoms with no idea what was going on with their brain, and they have endured the havoc a TBI can cause in their day-to-day lives. Proper testing and therapy could have avoided this. Others find themselves on medications and in rehabilitation for years. It's an injury that can turn your life upside down and create chaos in the lives of all those around you. Not until I experienced my own TBI did I fully realize the impact such an injury can have on one's life.

I write to tell everyone that there are different ways to handle your injury, there are ways to cope and endure this confusing and life-altering event and, yes, you can become the person you once were, or at least, close to it. It's the Silent Warrior in all of us that will help get you there.

THE GLORIOUS LIFE

Kurtz, Toranado and Broer

I woke to another glorious day on my little ranch in Bandera, Texas. The sun was full and the pastures abundant with wildflowers. My Friesian horses, Broer and Toranado, called to me for their breakfast as they always do and I felt that quiet satisfaction in my soul that I was not only needed, but I was loved. While feeding the horses I give a hug to my miniature Sicilian donkey, Lilly, an animal that lives for attention and love. I breathe in the sweet aroma of hay and the morning air. The Texas hills surround my property and I take a moment to view the mist that is now just rising above their peaks. If there is a heaven on earth, I count myself in its midst daily.

Returning to the house, my two imported German Shepherds, Taboo and Kurtz, bouncing about my feet, I take a few moments to sit on the bench and spend some time among the century-old oaks that I lovingly care for. There are over 400 trees on my property and I'm a big believer in being a good steward of the land; that includes the trees. I can't help but wonder what stories they could tell — the people who must have cared for them before me and the battles fought on their land. The lovers they watched over and the seasons they endured.

After a bowl of fruit on the back deck, a cup of coffee and a snuggle with my Mekong Bobtail, Bobo the Cat, after a bit more gazing at the hills, I will begin my day as I always do, at my desk, typing grants and exploring ways to raise money for the nonprofit I founded back in 1998, the Moonlight Fund. The fund cares for burn survivors and their families. Chosen as the top nonprofit in the country in 2012, it has continued to grow and receive both awards and national recognition. I was burned as a child and know personally the needs of those I serve. Nearly 22 years, numerous awards and 12,000 people later, I'm still as invested in this mission of mine as I was in 1998. I accept no salary, I donate my book and speaking proceeds to the fund, and I cherish all those we've helped with this mighty mission of ours. It's the toughest job I've ever had, yet the most satisfying and rewarding work I could ever imagine. I have found that a life of service suits me perfectly. I am rewarded with the hugs and love of those I serve.

I could not have done any of this without the loving support of my husband, Randy. God, I loved that man. Like no other man I had ever met before in my life, he captured a space in my heart and spirit that took me to vast heights and allowed me new adventures in life. Whether I was hunting by his side or simply enjoying morning coffee with him, it was always good. In addition, he also provided me the opportunity to remain at home, working, dedicating my time, pro bono, to the fund. Randy was also a financial donor. He was as emotionally involved in this mission of mine as I was, and the gratefulness I felt in my heart for his sacrifices was huge.

To manage all this, Randy had to accept work overseas and across the country. In our nearly nine years together, we only had a few months of actually living together full time. We made the most of his visits home, yet they were short. It was a sacrifice we both lived with silently. We hoped that one day retirement would come, and we would spend those long-awaited evenings on the back deck together or wrapped in one another's arms. The goodbyes were tough, yet we faced them time and time again to carry on this mission.

I felt blessed daily that once my work was done, I could head out to the barn for my longed-for ride on one or both of my horses. I had access to over 2,000 acres for riding and I loved exploring the hills, inlets and the river. Wildlife was plentiful here and I enjoyed coming across some wild turkeys or the obvious signs of a mountain lion. The birds overhead were plentiful and the past few years we'd had our share of bald eagles. I also loved riding under a full moon — it's an exhilarating feeling to be alone with your horse, navigating the trees with just the light of the moon and the spirits we can only imagine among us. A breathtaking experience on many levels, and something I did as often as I could.

Beyond everything, I loved working the land. I had a ranch hand who provided some help in the barn a few days a week, but the bulk of the work was mine to enjoy. I aerated, harrowed and overseeded my pastures. I also hand-pulled any weed or rock I saw and after having done so for many years, my pastures resembled something more like you'd see in Kentucky than Texas. I loved feeling the dirt on my body, mixed with my own sweat, the sore muscles and the satisfaction of a long day's work.

My grandfather owned a farm in Wisconsin. I spent many a weekend and summers working that land and developed a keen sense of land management and a strong sense of being a good steward of the land. He taught me so many things that I am grateful for today. Other than riding my horses, I was happiest when I was working the land. It brought satisfaction to my soul in addition to creating a good footing and a rich food source for my horses. The cycle of life was in full view for me there and I enjoyed nothing more than watching its beauty, season after season.

I often asked myself, why do I deserve this life? That peace and tranquil existence. Was it because I spent my time caring for those less fortunate, or maybe because I endured and survived an abusive childhood? Somehow, I ended up here and each day I thanked the gods for it. I was keenly aware that not everyone has such beauty to take in each day — there are plenty of people still fighting the fight. I knew because I cared for many of them. So, I felt I must remain ever grateful for the place in this world that I inhabited, for it was truly a gift from the gods.

As on all days, I fit in a bit more work for the Moonlight Fund, closed my office for the day, took in the magnificent sunset on my back deck and waited for the phone to ring. My nightly calls from Randy were food for my soul and my heart. I'd learned to live alone and had done so for quite some time, yet I was not immune to the moments when the lonely creeps in. I loved to hear his voice, and although Randy was a man of few words, our nightly chats were the highlight of my day. He was quick to ask about the animals, my day and how the Moonlight Fund was doing. I loved the nights when I actually had some new news to share that might extend our conversation, for I dreaded the fact that most nights he would need to get to bed early, as he rose quite early for work. I had found that when you treasure the smallest of things in life, they become large things, and my nightly conversations with Randy were large things. They were truly the highlight of my day, the song of my night, and I'd even say they were fine competition for the sunsets.

Sunset from my back porch

BUILDING MY BACKBONE

My brother Mark and I

Now that I've painted a rosy picture for you, allow me to tell you how I came to this point in my life and share the events that truly formed my backbone. My childhood was like something out of a really bad movie. My alcoholic father was abusive and violent. My mother, brother and I lived in a world of constant fear and turmoil. When I was just 21 months of age, my mother was boiling a pot of bottles on the stove for my baby brother. I heard my brother's cries from down the hall as my mother was changing his diaper and, as any big sister would wish to do, I only wanted to help. My cries and gestures towards the boiling pot — my toddler's way of helping fetch a bottle for my brother — infuriated my father, who, as you would imagine, was drinking at the time. His response was to throw the pot of boiling water over my head. My mother heard my screams and rushed to my side. To her horror, as she removed my shirt my skin came off with it. I was rushed to the hospital and would teeter between life and death for some time before the grafting process could begin.

This event, as so many in my life, was kept secret. I spent most of my life with many secrets. Each morning I stood motionless as my mother covered my scars with thick Dermablend® makeup and carefully chose clothing that would cover my scars. I would undergo dozens of surgeries in my young life and even more as a young adult.

Yet, I will say, the abuse my father piled on me and my brother did not come close to what I witnessed him do to my mother. This had a much bigger impact on me. To watch my mother beaten, time and time again. To sit with her as she filled the bathtub with blood was excruciating for a little girl. I did my best to protect her. I was so small, yet, I would get in between them and fight my best to keep him off her. I had no fear of him hurting me in those moments — I was filled with rage, I was a tiny Warrior and I was out to protect my mother from another bloody beating. This was in the '60s, when people looked the other way. I often ran to the neighbor's home pleading for help and was turned away. I was on my own. No help would come and although I many times felt helpless, I never stopped trying to fight him off.

There was one area of his abuse that I could not fight off, and that was the sexual abuse. I have blocked many of those memories. I can only assume that I stayed quiet out of fear, or perhaps I thought that it was better that I take the abuse than my mother. Either way, I had to endure it, and endure it I did.

When I was twelve, my mother gave birth to my baby sister, Audra. I can remember the excitement I felt at the thought of a baby entering our household — perhaps this new addition would stop the rage that we lived with day after day. I remember the day my mother went into labor; she drove me to a bar and asked that I go in and retrieve my father. A humiliating thing for a child to do. I was a small girl at twelve and I can still remember entering that bar and slowly walking down the aisle by the bar stools until I came to my father, sitting with another woman. I looked up at him and said "Daddy, the baby is coming, can you please come home?" I remember the look of irritation on his face, yet he came.

The next morning, I woke to one of the most joyful things I'd ever seen. A piece of paper with a baby's footprint on it, and above the footprint was the name Audra. I had begged my parents to allow me to name the baby Audra, after a character in the Big Valley television show that I adored. I finally had a light in my life and when they brought Audra home, I was in love and I was sure that my family would now heal with this precious gift we had been given. Surely a baby would make everything wonderful again. Right? How could she not?

Things were a bit quieter for a while. When Audra was two months old and my brother 10 and I 12, my father suggested a family get-away at a nice place in Wisconsin. His plan was to send us up and he'd join us in a couple days. As two, then three, days passed I noticed the anguish on my mother's face. I for one was more than happy to have the time without my father. I spent countless hours caring for Audra and plenty of time out on the dock fishing.

Finally, my mother's fears got the best of her and she packed us up and we headed home. Once home the truth was quickly evident. The cars were missing from the drive, and as we walked into the house we saw the furnishings were all gone. My mother rang the airport and sure enough, my fathers' plane had been gone for days. The next day a trip to the bank revealed more bad news — the bank accounts had been emptied. My mother was left with three children, an empty home, one vehicle and little else. Efforts to find my father were fruitless. We heard that he had found his way to Australia. We were penniless and on our own.

My mother was an astute, incredibly bright woman. It did not take her long to enroll in college to complete her degree in accounting. Although I was only 12, I knew my role would be to help raise Audra and Mark. I also knew that I would need to help bring some cash into the household. I got odd jobs and did just that. I became a parent to my siblings at the age of 12 and I do not regret it. It helped form who I am today, and it was what was needed at the time. We survived. Not an easy survival, but survival without the evil of my father.

Mark joined the Navy at age 17 and Audra eventually went off to college. I was fortunate. I had to drop out of school in the eighth grade to raise my siblings, but I was very blessed to have a good head on my shoulders and a savvy business sense. I was off on a path in life that would take me far in business and in relationships. Although this childhood of mine may have been rocky, it prepared me to be a tough negotiator, savvy businesswoman and a true survivor. Throughout my life and all the challenges that would come my way, I found my stepping stones laid out before me like a masterpiece. The Warrior in me was taking shape and would see me on my path to success.

Audra, Mom and I

Kissing Valhalla

Riding Broer in the fall

July 12 of 2017 was like any other day. The weather was cooler than normal, and I began my day with a good workout and a few hours in the office. I was still on Cloud 9 and enjoying a good tan from my trip to Puerto Rico. Moonlight Fund had organized a retreat for seven women caregivers to Puerto Rico a couple weeks previously. It was marvelous. Many of these women had spent years caring for not only their husbands who had suffered burn injuries, but also being full-time moms, so to give them this trip was truly special. It was a blessing to see them let loose, come out of their shells and enjoy themselves on an entirely new level. The trip was sponsored by Chive Charities and we will forever be grateful to them for providing such a wonderful outlet for these deserving women. Moonlight Fund cannot do what we do without the support of such generous sponsors. To this day, we are dependent on our donors and their generosity.

Early in the afternoon, one of the retreat attendees, Bethany Coomes, rang me and asked if she might come by and spend some time. Bethany and I had become quite close on the trip and I always enjoyed her visits. She and I had developed a deep connection, a connection built on trust and love. The interesting thing about Bethany and her family was that her husband, Clayton, was a military burn unit nurse at Brooke Army Medical Center and worked alongside me during the Iraq war. Then, as fate would have it, their daughter, Stella,

14

was burned years later. So, as a family, they came back into the Moonlight Fund fold. I believe fate brought us together in many ways, for she is my most treasured and beloved friend.

As I awaited Bethany's arrival, I finished up some last-minute business for the Moonlight Fund and tidied up the house. I loved spending time with Bethany. And as we were sitting on the back deck, taking in the amazing hills that surround my property and reminiscing about our trip to Puerto Rico, she suggested we go for a ride. Although Bethany is a novice rider, I knew my horse Broer could be trusted with her on his back. Broer is one of the most solid horses I've ever owned or ridden. I knew she would be safe in his care.

That is the last of my memories from that day. What I share from this point on is all recalled by Bethany, medical staff and my husband Randy.

I saddled up both horses and off we went. We rode out to a remote area on an old, narrow asphalt road bordered by dense trees and lined with barbed wire, out in the middle of nowhere. I had often told people not to ride there. I would never ride there, I called it a death trap; yet, that is where we found ourselves when all hell broke loose. Why, to this day I ask myself, were we riding in such dangerous terrain? I will never know.

As Bethany recalls, my horse, Toranado, took off running. It was something he did regularly, and I was quite accustomed to it. He was always a handful and that was one of the things I enjoyed most about him — I love a horse with spirit. She also recalls that I attempted to spin him to the left, something I also did regularly with great success, but this time it did not work. He was at a full run, completely out of control. I could have run this out, as I was quite accustomed to doing. But I knew Bethany could not.

The horse Bethany was on, Broer, took up with the running, and although I have no memories of it, I know exactly what I did next. I had a novice rider, my friend Bethany, on a 1700-pound horse. I needed to stop both my horse and hers because I knew Broer would not stop while Toranado was still running full tilt — knowing Toranado, I'd estimate we were going 40 miles an hour. So I threw the reins, braced myself, and screamed "hold on" to Bethany. I pushed off Toranado, throwing my leg behind me over the saddle to get clear.

Bethany at this point had lost both stirrups and was doing her best just to hold on. Just after she leaned down to pass under a low branch...she saw it. She saw me push off and as if it were in slow motion, she watched my body sail through the air. But instead of the tuck-and-roll dismount I had planned, my head hit first on the hard asphalt and my body followed with a loud thump. I lay motionless on the asphalt road.

Her mount, Broer, came to a complete stop and made his way slowly towards me, allowing her to safely dismount. She was about 15 yards from me and even at that distance she could tell that there were no obvious signs of life. She rushed to my side and Broer followed her. My maneuver had worked. Broer had stopped running and Bethany was safe, but at a great cost to my life.

Bethany's military medical training came in handy and she knew not to move me and how to check my vitals. My lips were quivering, and my eyes were rolling to the back of my head. All color had left my body, my Puerto Rico tan was completely gone. Bethany described my coloring as yellow.

My breath was shallow, barely there, and Bethany placed her mouth over mine to offer me some air. It worked, and my breathing increased at that point. She slowly ran her hand under my head. To her horror, as she delicately removed her hand, it was covered in blood. The pool of blood would continue to grow as time went by and she frantically called for help. She called out to the skies, "Not on my watch...Celia Belt...you will not die on my watch!"

There were no landmarks or homes in view other than a distant water tower. Bethany looked around and then she noticed, as Broer stood there motionless, that her cell phone was at his feet. She called 911. Luckily a paramedic from California, here visiting his parents, heard the call on his scanner and drove his truck through brush and bramble to get to us. He attended to me and guided the ambulance through. I will be forever grateful to this young man. In all honesty, he probably saved my life. He might as well have been on a white horse as driving a white truck — he truly was my savior on that day. As I was loaded into the ambulance Bethany was not about to leave my side and approached the front of the vehicle to get in. The driver flatly refused, noting the amount of blood on her hands and clothing. At this point, a few people had gathered, and one kind soul approached Bethany with a bottle of water and washed her hands clean of my blood, so she was allowed to ride with me to the hospital. She rode in the front of the ambulance, still in shock, staring down at her once blood-stained hands. Looking back at me for any signs of life, all she heard were my moans. She pleaded with the driver to drive faster, because to her, it seemed, we were crawling to our destination and it was taking forever to reach a level-one trauma center in San Antonio.

It was 11:30 that night before I came to. I began uttering my husband's phone number, over and over. I could not get the entire number out, only bits and pieces, yet I kept attempting to say his number. The vertigo was intense, the room was spinning, and I could not stop vomiting. The pain in my head was excruciating. I looked around the room and there stood Bethany and two of my Moonlight Fund wives, Valeria Seguritan and April Lage. The next day another Moonlight Fund wife, Leigh Ann Kenney, came to look after me. The expression on their faces was a mixture of shock and horror and a bit of disgust. I knew, somewhere deep in my heart, that I had caused hurt to these women that I loved so dearly. I had let them down. Somewhere in my heart I knew that I had let down the women I loved the most. Something I would need to live with in the future.

The nurse informed me that I was in University Hospital and would have to be moved to the neurosurgical unit due to the need to have surgery to reduce the bleeding on my brain. I had suffered a subarachnoid hemorrhage; my brain was bleeding.

My only response was, "Why am I here and not at Baptist or Methodist, I have good insurance?" Her response was, "You needed to be in a level-one trauma center." Throughout the night I underwent several scans to determine the extent of bleeding in my brain. Early the next morning the attending neurosurgeon made the decision not to operate. I will never know if that decision was the right one. Was the untreated swelling on my brain the later cause of my seizures, lack of brain function and my permanently ruptured inner ear? Should they have gone ahead and relieved the swelling? I'll never know. I've received different opinions from several doctors. In the end, it simply is what it is.

During my three days in the hospital I was never alone. Moonlight Fund wives and mothers took shifts and were always by my side and my husband, Randy, drove 17 hours straight to be by my side. I was told that two lobes of my brain were damaged, and the vestibular between my brain and my inner ear was damaged also. They ran MRIs and CT scans frequently, yet they never ran an EEG. It would be months before I would know the full extent of the brain damage.

Although I did not fully realize it, my life changed on that day and would never be the same again. My life, as the uber-powerful founder of the Moonlight Fund, public speaker and astute businesswoman, was essentially over.

A part of me felt robbed. I had always said, "I'll go off the back of a horse, my Valhalla." Yet, this was not to be my Valhalla...there were things to come in my life. Things that would need my attention, things only the gods understood.

Thinking back to the evening of the injury, my daughter, Hillary, had been visiting my place. As she was enjoying sitting on the back deck, my horse Toranado appeared, his bridle gone and no rider on his back. She knew immediately that I had been hurt. The fear that ripped through her breaks my heart to this day. I've always been a fearless rider; yet, I know that has caused some fear among those I love, and, on this day, it caused the ultimate pain in my poor daughter's heart. She had no idea where I was or if I was alive or dead. This experience also had an impact on Bethany; she lived with guilt for months. She had suggested we ride that day and it has haunted her ever since. Although I attempted to explain to her that all in this life happens for a reason, she blamed herself and lived with the awful memories of what she had seen take place. She had to continue to work through these memories as she spent time with me and saw firsthand the damage done to my brain. It took some time, but I believe she finally began to understand that yes, all things happen for a reason, often reasons we cannot understand. My fearless ways have caused pain to others on more than one occasion and on this day, I regretted my actions fully.

Although, if asked, would I do it all again...would I risk my life to save the life of another rider...my answer would be... yes...I'd do it again.

Bethany and I at the accident site

Bethany describing how she lifted my head

CHOOSE YOUR BATTLES WISELY

Wondering if there is any hope

Once home, the world was still spinning, the vertigo was constant, and the headaches were unceasing. I joked that vertigo was the best way to redecorate your home while never moving a thing. This went on for eight weeks. I also had little control of my bladder, an embarrassing thing to say the least. I had appointments with my neurosurgeon, Dr. Thomas Kingman, and my ear surgeon, Dr. Charles Symms. Home health care was scheduled, and I was cared for by nurses, physical therapists and occupational therapists in my home, in addition to my daughter, Hillary, who moved in temporarily. Randy stayed for a few days, but was needed back at work and although I could tell he was concerned for me, I also sensed he was disappointed in me. My reckless ways were getting the best of him and he was nearing the end of his patience. I feared losing him. I prayed I wouldn't.

I was prescribed far too many drugs, at least in my opinion. I truly thought nothing was wrong, other than the world kept spinning due to the vertigo, I could not control the vomiting and I lived with constant headaches and loads of medications. I was quite certain that I'd be writing grants and accepting speaking engagements within a few weeks' time — this was just a little setback. Once again, I thought I knew all the answers to something and I did as I wanted and I was wrong, I felt like quite a fool. I was not following doctors' orders, thinking I was just fine, not getting the rest my brain so badly needed, and in the end, I paid for it. I paid a heavy price in the months and years to follow.

My world continued to spin for those weeks due to the vertigo and I endured the constant vomiting, stumbling about, and frequent falls. Once that slowed down, I began to imagine just how I could kick-start my brain, what could I do to begin thinking clearly again? I had the novel idea that if I took up playing card games on my laptop, something I'd never done in the past, that I would somehow regain some sort of brain activity. So I sat for hours, playing one card game after another, only to be reprimanded by my neurosurgeon, Dr. Kingman, when I divulged my activities to him. He explained that was probably the worst thing I could be doing with a brain injury. He explained that my brain needed rest, not activity, that I should be home, in bed, resting and getting as much sleep as possible. Being still has never been my strong suit. I was frustrated and once again felt like a complete fool. I realized it was time I best start listening to my doctors. I was certainly not getting any better and I was realizing that I possessed none of the answers.

I was unable to shower for weeks until Randy purchased a stool for me to sit in the shower. Ah, it felt so wonderful to feel the water flow over my body after so many weeks of sponge baths. As I sat there, I recalled memories of the waterfalls in Puerto Rico and how refreshing the water felt on my body and the exhilaration of jumping off the cliffs. Then, my eyes caught something at the bottom of the shower, a large mass of hair. It startled me, and at first I couldn't think where that amount of hair could have come from. Then, I reached up to my head, to the site of my wound. It measured approximately seven inches long by three inches at its widest point and was still quite tender. There was no hair in this area, and I realized that the hair I was staring down at was mine. I've always been a bit vain about my long, thick hair and it was truly a sad moment to sit there and see so much of it bundled in a mass at my feet. Sadly, it would not end there. I continued to lose hair from all areas of my head for the next 14 months. My doctors had no real answer as to why this was happening, if it was the trauma to my head, the stress of the event or, perhaps, the medication I was taking. For months I stood and cried as I showered and looked down at my feet at the mass of hair. It did eventually slow in its loss and today I have thicker hair, although the area of the wound site has never completely regained all its hair and my once thick hair is now just medium in thickness. My vanity took a blow, but I was alive and that was what mattered.

I had no earthly idea how to get better and I was willing to try anything to get some semblance of me back. I found myself having outrageous outbursts at the people I loved. My doctors explained this was all part of my brain injury and would get better in time. TIME...?...I didn't have time.... I needed to get back to work and I sure as hell did not want to hurt the people I loved the most. My husband and my daughter were subjected to my rage and I had no idea how to control it or where it was coming from. I was becoming someone else, someone I did not know, and I was unwilling to stand by and let this happen. I had to find a way to get better, I had to find a way to control this awful madness that had taken over my brain. I had to survive, and I certainly did not like this new version of me.

It was a whole new level of crazy that I had never experienced and could not control. To say nothing of the odd and eerie feeling in my head that came and went, the "shaking" sensation, in my brain. Day and night, the shakes would come, sometimes waking me from sleep. At the time I wondered what it was, why did my brain feel like it was shaking inside my head? I'll be honest: It terrified me, it felt like someone was in my head and was shaking my brain, so I kept it to myself and I suffered these episodes in silence.

Broer, peace in the pasture

MY TABOO

Taboo

Before my accident, in April of 2017, I had imported another German Shepherd from the Czech Republic, Taboo, and had given some thought to him being trained for TBIs (traumatic brain injury) since my other Shepherd, Kurtz, was trained for PTSDs. My dogs were used in my work with burn survivors — many were wounded military and for years the dogs had played an integral part in the Moonlight Fund's work. Just weeks before, I had had a conversation with one of the military dog trainers I co-trained my dogs with, mentioning the need for a TBI dog.

After my accident Taboo's training came to a stop. He remained by my side as I lay in bed. Many times, he was in the bed with me, gently placing his head on my chest or in the nook of my neck. He did this for weeks, never leaving my side. I felt terribly guilty that his training had been put on hold, yet I was grateful for his constant companionship and unconditional love. Although I had nurses, friends and family to help, it was Taboo that was my full time source of support.

A couple months after my accident, Greg, one of the trainers I'd worked with years before, paid me a visit. As we sat and talked about old times, he suddenly became sullen and a bit serious. Looking me right in the eye, he said, "Celia, we need to train Taboo for you, as a Traumatic Brain Injury Service dog." My response to this was, "I will not need him; perhaps someone else will." Yet, his gaze was firm, and in my heart, I knew what he was saying was the truth. I was never going to be the same and I was going to need all the help I could find, canine and human. My heart broke just a little, yet, I knew he was right.

Funny how fate finds you. This new dog, Taboo, would go on to be trained as a TBI dog, not so much for my charitable work, but as my service dog. To this day, he accompanies me everywhere, whether by plane or by car. Book signings, speaking engagements, meetings with donors — he is a constant by my side. At first, I had to get over the embarrassment of having a service dog; now, I stand proud to have Taboo at my side for all things and at all times. He senses my seizures and also assists with my vertigo and balance issues. I feel safe when he places his paw on me during a seizure or leans against me during a bad vertigo episode. He was by my side when I lost my baby sister, then my husband...and has been with me all the time I have spent mourning the two of them. We are never apart. It's an odd thing to admit, but I spend 24/7 with a dog. He brings me peace, companionship and above all else, he brings me safety and a huge sense of joy.

I will share this: I do get some looks and questions as to why I have a service dog. A traumatic brain injury is an invisible injury, so many people are curious as to why I have a service dog by my side. A TBI is much like PTSD; it's a hidden part of ourselves that the rest of the world cannot see or understand. It can be a bit uncomfortable to have a service dog under these circumstances; people do stare and wonder.

I've also run into people with visible injuries who are not shy about showing their disdain and jealousy that I have a service dog and they do not. It's just something I must live with. I wish I could give each and every one of them a service dog. I do my best to meet their eyes with kindness and understanding. I realize that I am blessed to have this dog, my constant and caring companion.

My doctors had finally released me to work out, but only under the guidance of a skilled trainer and at minimal levels. After a couple months I was finally allowed to use the elliptical. I was ecstatic to be progressing! As I was carefully pacing myself on this machine with Taboo by my side, a woman approached me and screamed at me to get my dog out of the facility. The gym is located in my neighborhood and is there for the use of the homeowners. This particular woman had been hired to oversee the common areas and obviously felt it her right to govern whether or not a service animal should be allowed in the gym. Taboo was wearing his vest and I offered to show her all his documents. I carefully descended from the machine and retrieved the five separate documents that were placed in Taboo's vest. She threw them back at me and said, "Get out or I'll call the police." There were two men working out in the room and neither of them came to my aid. I think that hurt the worst. I was very shaky and beside myself, not knowing what to do. She obviously had no idea of the laws regarding service animals, yet I was terrified. I ranted a few words her way and left. Walking to my home a short distance away, I could not believe what had just taken place. Taboo accompanies me everywhere, on planes, to restaurants, during events; I am never without him.

Once home I experienced rolling seizures brought on by the stress of the event. At the time, I had some contractors working on the house. They had come to know me well enough that they knew something was very wrong. They helped me sit down and calmed me, asking what had happened and how could they help.

I also shared what had happened with my friends and my dog trainer. They encouraged me to report the woman. I'm not one to stir up problems, yet I knew this needed to be done to protect me and all others with service dogs. One of the wounded soldiers I had cared for years ago and who had remained a good friend put it best, "You stand strong in all ways to care for us, yet you will not stand to take care of yourself." I made the necessary calls to HUD and Texas Disabilities. In the end, my neighborhood payed a hefty fine, which I chose to donate to a facility that trains service dogs. They also had to undergo training for service dog awareness. It was an ugly scene, one I wish had not happened.

For those of you with brain injuries or other life-altering injuries — if at all possible, I highly recommend finding a service dog. There are many facilities that place dogs at a nominal charge or for free. There are also training facilities that you can take your own dog to for service training. The companionship and care are well worth it.

Taboo has literally saved my life many a time. Not only by alerting me to seizures, but also by steadying me during vertigo, watching over me during sleepwalking incidents and literally helping to lift me up after a bad fall. I also never fear living alone in a remote area. He is my caregiver and my protector on so many levels.

In November of 2019 I added to my little family and imported another German Shepherd. She was also bred by the same German judge that I had purchased my previous dogs from. Little Risqué has brought a spot of joy to me, Taboo and our entire household.

Celia with her pups, Risqué and Taboo

WHEN THE SKY FALLS

Bethany and I at the accident site

Just when I was beginning to feel like I had a handle on things, the pieces of the sky began to tumble down on me, one by one. Since the accident I had paid several visits to my optometrist — there were too many times when I simply could not read, even with the best of magnifying glasses. He repeatedly told me my sight was fine. I knew better. It was happening far too often, and words were disappearing before my eyes, for long periods of time.

A little later, I underwent a series of tests with my ear surgeon and was told that I had lost the lion's share of my hearing and would need hearing aids. I flatly refused — my vanity came out in full force and I would not wear hearing aids. I also believed my body would heal itself. I was in complete denial that my hearing was so badly affected. Further testing showed that the inner vestibular, between my brain and ear, was "permanently" ruptured. This would also account for my eyesight problems. I had to accept the fact that my balance would never be the same and the vertigo and sight issues would always be a part of my life. There was no "fixing" these issues. I also had to accept that awful shaking sensation in my brain that terrified me each time it took place.

I was dealing with lifetime injuries and it was important that I not only accept them as such, but that I seek the proper treatment and apply myself to that treatment. Yet, once again, my stubborn streak came out. Although I was on meds for the vertigo, I could not imagine an existence where falls would be a regular part of life or accept that the room spinning would simply be something I would have to live with. I was determined to find a way to fix this or at least modify it as best I could. How could I possibly accept speaking engagements and risk a fall, or the room spinning? I had to find a way to get better and if the doctors told me there was no way, well then, I would find a better way to cope. I was not going to just give up and take this diagnosis as is, yet the better part of me knew I had to. I also wondered, how would this affect my riding? Balance is extremely important to riding. My head was spinning, literally.

This was nothing more than another challenge in this long life of mine and face it head on was what I was prepared to do. If I was not going to get better, I was determined to seek out ways to learn to live this way. Yet, I didn't like the new me. I wanted the old me back. I was suffering in such silence that I could almost hear the silence. But I would adapt to the new me, come hell or high water. I simply could not sit back and let my disability take me over. I was in for a hell of a ride, I just didn't know it. This ride was for a lifetime.

Additional side effects of a brain injury that continued to catch me off guard were the outbursts of anger I showered on those I loved. My husband, children and friends, no one was immune from my rage. Dr. Kingman's nurse had explained that this was to be expected with a subarachnoid hemorrhage. I could not believe the way I found myself yelling at my daughter and husband over the smallest of things. The rage that spewed from my mouth as if I was possessed. The pain in their eyes was palpable — they were doing their best to accept this new side of me and I'm certain they hoped it would soon all pass as my health got better. Of all the side effects of a brain injury, I would say this was one of the most painful, hurting those I loved with my rage that came from a mind that I no longer understood or could control. All I could do was cry after these incidents and beg for their forgiveness. I was helpless at controlling my egregious behavior.

I also worried about sex. I had no sex drive for quite some time. This would surely complicate my relationship with Randy. I found a few articles on the web regarding sex drive and brain injuries, but they made me feel even more hopeless. I was going to have to do all I could to retrigger that part of my brain. Randy was already showing signs of frustration and I simply could not lose him. Our sex life was always a big part of our relationship. I finally came across an article that offered some hope and although I will not share all its secrets here, I did all it suggested, and it worked. Randy and I were back on track to a loving, sexual relationship. Although I will say, many times I found my head reeling with vertigo and that strange shaking sensation in my brain. But, wow, was I thankful for the progress made in this area of our lives! Perhaps there was hope for us after all.

Another lovely part of a brain injury one must deal with is depression and anxiety. I'd never dealt with either at any time in my life. I knew these issues would probably present themselves. I had attended a TBI training class during my days as a volunteer on the burn unit. When these issues did strike, I was prepared to do battle with them and not let them get the best of me. If you know the enemy is coming, you are better off putting on your armor and waiting, because the battle is coming and it's a very real battle, I can assure you of that.

Be honest with those around you about what you're feeling. Let your doctors know, and if there are meds available to help, take them. When you're depressed, go out and do something fun and stay active. Don't let anxiety eat you alive, because she will. Change your routine, work out, visit with friends, go to a movie, do anything, but don't do nothing. You can beat these two demons. I assure you of that. But it takes an effort; some days it takes a whole damn army. You'll need to grab the bull by the horns and make that effort or you'll fall into a deep, dark place that I promise you will not enjoy.

Broer and I

EEG, THE ENLIGHTENMENT

Enjoying one of my favorite century-old oaks

A few months after the accident, my neurosurgeon, Dr. Kingman, was about to give me a good bill of health and refer me out to a neurologist. I had undergone several MRIs and CT scans and although I still did not feel like "Celia," I was progressing, or so we thought. I was still having the odd shaking in my brain, the bouts of vertigo and frequent falls.

Then, it happened, one fateful day. I awoke at eight and fed the horses. The next memory I have is of me lying in the front of my property, the horses loose, my dogs at my side. It was 11:15. I had lost three hours and had no memory of any of the events that had taken place during that time. I would never endanger my horses in such a way, setting them loose outside of their pasture. Something was seriously wrong, and I was plenty frightened.

I rang my neurosurgeon's office to report this and it was at this point that they ordered an EEG, a test that until this point had not been done. I cannot stress enough, if you have a head injury, get an EEG. It may take more than one or two EEGs to fully diagnose your brain injury, but insist the test be performed. It can answer so many unanswered questions. I have worked with far too many patients who have had head injuries and when only scans have been performed it has been evident to me that something else is going on — an EEG could offer them some answers, as it certainly did for me.

There is something wrong with our system when so many people with brain injuries do not undergo an EEG. Scans alone cannot disclose the whole picture of what damage has been done to the brain. The information provided by the EEG was a shocking eye opener for me, and it changed the course of my treatment and my entire life.

I had the EEG on a Tuesday and thought very little of it. The next Monday I noticed that my email, phones and fax lines had been blown up with messages from my neurosurgeon's office the previous Friday. I rang the office and they frantically informed me that I was having seizures and said I should continue taking the Keppra (anti-seizure) medication.

Seizures...I could not fathom that I was having seizures on top of all of my other symptoms. Just the word itself terrified me. I informed them I had only been given two weeks' worth of the medication when I left the hospital more than a month ago and had not been taking it for some time. They called in a new prescription for Keppra and to this day I am on this and a second antiseizure med. I also have a third medication I take during seizures. I don't like taking these medications and wish I could reduce all of them. I feel like a slave each day as I stand before my list of drugs my nurses have prepared for me. I methodically lay out each pill next to its name and picture. (It took several months for my nurses to develop a system for me, I was often confused and taking the wrong pills.) There are many days I cry as I lay out the pills, then recheck them, then count them. I cry just because the prospect of taking these medications for rest of my life is overwhelming. Yet, I know I must follow the course and do all I can to maintain my health at the highest level. My doctors have informed me that this is a lifelong injury, requiring lifelong care. I must accept and embrace that. It is not an easy thing, to accept. Yet accept it I must.

I still run into people whom I've known for years, but I have no memory of them. I continue to forget what I was walking through the house to fetch; my memory is certainly not working on all gears. It's a different life for me. I've developed a set of lists and tasks that help me work through my days. Some days it works, other days it doesn't. I will share with you that a huge piece of my heart is sad, sad that the old Celia is not here, and probably never will be. All I can do is make plans for the new Celia, make each day work as best I can and try not to mourn too much for the loss I have suffered.

Shortly after receiving this new information from Dr. Kingman I rang Randy. I knew that I had to share this news with him. I also knew it would be tough for him to accept. His wife, the independent, astute businesswoman who hunted by his side, worked the land, shared his bed, was now dealing with a critical and permanent brain and inner ear injury. Randy loved the strong woman he married and I could hear it in his voice...he was heartbroken. Perhaps I even heard that he was a little less in love.

Hell, I was a little less in love with me. I was angry, frustrated and heartbroken each time a doctor told me I would never ride a horse again, drive a car, have the ability to run my nonprofit. I couldn't even write out a check or count change. I had lost the ability to complete the simplest of tasks and to do those things I loved the most. I felt like I was lost in a deep, dark mist, somewhere I'd never been before, and I could not find my way back.

A few years back I attended a class out on Fort Sam Houston in San Antonio regarding traumatic brain injuries. We were seeing so many of these injuries during the war. I began to remember some of what I had learned, and I wished I didn't. I began to remember all the complex side effects of these injuries. I knew several wounded military members with TBIs. Some were doing OK, some were not, several had committed suicide. What category would I fall in, would I ever be me again? Or was it impossible? I swayed between helplessness and depression to deep-down determination.

I would say this to anyone who has experienced a brain injury: Do not rely on the scans to fully diagnose what your brain has just experienced. It is only with the additional testing of not one, but sometimes several, EEGs that you will know if there is seizure activity or other brain or inner ear damage that you must address. It's also important to seek the care of an ear surgeon. I would never have imagined the damage my inner ear received in this accident and how it has affected my life. Be diligent and seek all the testing you can. It's only with knowledge that you can find your path to better health. It's important to note that disability does not equal absolute inability.

Broer allowing me a quiet moment to cry

First My Mind, Now My Heart

Randy and I in Namibia, Africa

In August of 2017, my baby sister, Audra, who had been diagnosed with neuroendocrine cancer a few years back at age 37, rang to tell me she was covered head-to-toe with metastatic tumors and that the time was near. My immediate reaction was to fly and be by her side. My doctors forbade it — my brain was still in a fragile state. It wrenched my heart not to be by her side and it will haunt me forever that I was not with her when she crossed over on October 14, 2017.

Yet, there was more to come. On November 2, 2017, my husband, Randy, rang me. He was on a job site in Iowa. He went on to say that he had brain tumor. Honestly, with losing Audra, I had not been paying much attention to my own health and now with Randy telling me he had brain cancer I would be putting my own health even further on the back burner. My dog Taboo and I flew to Iowa on Thanksgiving Day. The Randy I once knew was gone. In such a short time he had become emaciated, slow and tired; yet he was still attempting to fight through it. He continued showing up on the job site, regardless of his weakened condition. He had every intention of having the tumor removed and returning to work. That simply was not reality. Although we agreed there would be no chemo or radiation, he was desperate to relieve the pressure on his brain. So, a few days later Randy's surgeon removed a tennis ball size portion of the tumor. This was not just any type of brain cancer; it was the deadliest, glioblastoma. I knew my time with my beloved Randy would soon come to an end.

After the surgery he was able to speak and communicate much like the old Randy I knew. As we sat on his hospital bed, he began to make plans for me after his passing. We spoke of many things, how his life would end, what drugs and the amount of those drugs he would be willing to take, and where he wanted to die.

When I told him I was too young to collect his Social Security widow's benefits, he was quite concerned. I went on to do some research and found that if I were to collect disability, I would qualify for a portion of my widow's benefits. When I mentioned this to him the next day he said, "Well, of course, you should have applied for disability months ago after your accident." But he knew that I am a very proud person. Accepting government assistance is something I never dreamed I would do. Yet, at this point I knew I might have no choice. I knew deep inside that I no longer had the ability to hold down a job. Randy was right, and I began the process, as gut-wrenching as it was for me. As soon as Randy was stable enough, I arranged for a medivac jet to bring him home. On December 6, 2017, we arrived in Texas. It was snowing, something quite rare in this part of Texas, and I knew God was bringing me the snow of my youth, the man I loved and the Texas I had grown to love.

The next morning, I glanced over the mail and I noticed a letter from the Texas State Medical Board. My driver's license had been revoked due to my brain injury and seizure activity. I had expected this would happen. Yet, for now, my health would need to be put on the back burner — all that mattered to me was caring for Randy, and nothing could come before that. I was functioning at an unusually high level for someone with my injuries, a blessing for sure because caring for Randy was a full-time job. Thankfully, Randy's dear friend, Mark Leicht, flew in and helped with Randy's care for the first week, and I also had the help of hospice.

On the morning of December 23, my friend Bethany rang me, and I mentioned that Randy was close. She packed up and drove the hour and a half to my house. The sky was odd that evening, not the usual stunning sunsets that cross the sky, but a dark, tornadic swirl that seemed to occupy only a portion of the sky. I'd never seen the sky like that before, nor since.

One thing I was fastidious about was keeping a fire in the fireplace 24/7 for Randy. On this day I could not get it going. No trick worked, and I gave up shortly before Bethany arrived. She also tried to get it going, but with no luck on this day.

It was a relief to have her there and we stepped out on the back deck and took in the odd nature of the sky. Then, out of nowhere, a large bird approached us out of the dark sky and as quickly as it approached it turned and flew away. We looked at one another with a strange sense of knowing and quickly ran into the house. I grabbed my stethoscope, leapt on top of Randy and heard just one faint last beat of Randy's heart. Randy crossed over on December 23 at 6:20. I lay with him there for nearly two hours, waiting for officials to arrive and during that time the fire that we had worked so hard to start... well, it started all on its own.

Audra and my son Justin during her last visit

CLIMBING THE WALL

Madame Regent Judy Callaway placing the DAR
Distinguished Citizen Medal on my lapel

With Randy gone, the house became very quiet. My partner was gone. My heart was void of any emotion and my mind blank. I spent hours recounting our time together, asking myself over and over again, had I made him happy or was I too much of a challenge? I knew that I would soon need to begin the process of gaining my disability benefits and the more heartbreaking task of living alone. Although I'd been living alone for quite some time, this was a whole new kind of alone. It's an alone I wish on no one.

I was also faced with the process of going through Randy's things. The garage was filled with his household goods from Iowa and the attic held box upon box of his memories that he had fastidiously packed away. It was a painful process to part with so many of his things. Thankfully, much went to friends and family, and I, of course, kept many special mementoes.

I knew I would also need to become serious about my recovery. Randy would expect me to get on with my life and do all I could to regain my health. Letting myself down was one thing, but I could never let Randy down. I loved him too much to ever let him down and that love did not end with his death.

In addition to setting up all my doctors' appointments, I attempted to jump right back into work. I was nearly finished with my book *Remarkably Intact*, and I busied myself with having friends over for dinner, and day-to-day activities. Yet, late at night, all the realities snuck their way back in

— the room still spent a good deal of time spinning due to my vertigo, my mind still did not function on all gears and the terrible shaking (seizures) were not dissipating. And of course, my heart was breaking for the loss of my sister and my husband.

My memory, well, I could remember some things, but most things were gone, and I desperately wanted my memories back. I'm not a magician. I couldn't just magically bring my memories back; they were gone, and I would have to accept that. I cannot fully explain the pain of losing so many memories. Most days I don't realize they are gone, then an incident will happen that will spur a moment of remembrance and nothing more. That is when it's really painful. That is when I realize I do not remember and I realize the memories are gone, no longer mine to treasure and cherish. They are simply gone, like a cloud that moves swiftly past and out of view within moments.

I found myself spending countless hours on my back deck. I had quite an aviary of birds on that back deck. I began feeding early in the season and included a wide variety of feed to attract myriad species of birds — hummingbirds, finches and doves, the list was endless. To say nothing of the numerous barn swallows that nested in my eaves each year. This year we had a wider variety than usual due to the hard winter up north. Many species of birds, those I'd grown up with in my youth, were now nesting here in Texas. It was glorious. As I sat and enjoyed their heavenly sound and viewed the new hatchings, I began to realize that it would soon all be gone and I'd have to wait till the next season to revel in their song and flight once again.

A sadness came over me at the thought of it; then, an idea struck me. I opened my computer and began researching what household birds had the widest range of song. After some time, I came across the Spanish Timbrado Canary. Certainly not the easiest bird to acquire, yet, after I listened to its song I knew this was the bird for me. I also knew I wanted a male; they have the widest range of song. A DNA test would need to be performed. I found an importer and ordered my bird. It took several months, and my hope was that my bird, Mr. Sashay as I named him, would arrive by Thanksgiving. I had a large event planned for the holiday and wanted to share Mr. Sashay with everyone. Well, as the universe would have it, three days before Thanksgiving I got the call. I rang a neighbor to take me to the post office to pick up my precious little guy. I had everything in place, his cage, food, bowls, a toy, and a thermometer to keep him at 74 degrees. I placed Mr. Sashay in his cage and sat marveling at his beauty and his song. He would sing back to me and it was glorious. Then, the third day, he tucked his head the entire day and would not sing, eat or move. The next day I found him dead. I rang my importer and packed Mr. Sashay back into his shipping crate. As I did, I saw an envelope attached to the exterior of the crate with bold writing: "READ THESE INSTRUCTIONS IMMEDIATELY." Inside were directions on how to care for your bird and a packet of supplements that were to be added to his water the first three days. I felt awful. I had literally killed Mr. Sashay. This brain of mine once again was not working on all gears. Needless to say, when Mr. Sashay 2 arrived eight months later, I followed all the instructions, and he has filled my life with such song and joy. I often find myself lying on the chaise, being lulled to sleep by his wide range of harmonious lullabies. My home is never quiet, and visitors are often quite shocked that such big and varied song could come from such a small bird. He's brought another level of joy to my home, and, thankfully, Bobo the cat has no interest in him.

Meanwhile, it was time for me to figure out a means of transportation. My schedule was filling up with doctors' appointments and most were either in Kerrville, 25 miles away, or in San Antonio, a nearly 50-mile ride, one way. I had heard of a service called ART, Alamo Regional Transit. They provided transportation at a nominal fee to those with disabilities. I rang them and was delighted that they said I qualified for assistance, although they did have limited hours of service in my area. Sounded easy enough to me — I could simply set my appointments to accommodate their schedule. I was so happy that I would not have to call friends and family to make the long drives.

Things quickly went south when my first ride never showed, my second ride was nearly an hour late and on my third try, they would not take cash. I gave up at that point and asked family and friends to help. There are no Ubers or taxis where I live. I would have to depend upon my loved ones. I hated to do it. I felt like such a burden, yet, I had no choice but to ask for help. In the end, it worked out pretty well. I found myself spending time with loved ones as I was chauffeured about. I made it fun by offering to buy them dinner or a trip to the nail spa. It all worked out well in the end. I spent two-plus years depending upon the charity of friends and family and yes, at times I found it humiliating. But we all made the best of it. We knew and hoped the day would come that I would once again be driving.

I felt quite alone. I spent many nights sitting on my back deck sobbing, wondering why Randy had to leave me now when I needed him the most. I gazed at the rising hills, listening to the music that reminded me of him, and I just cried. I mourned his death and my sister's death and I mourned the loss of my health. It seemed that all I loved had left me — all I had now was me, or what was left of me. Although I knew that with the help of my doctors, therapists, friends and daughter, I stood a fighting chance of regaining some of the "me" back. But, how long that would take and exactly what that would take, I did not know. I felt trapped in this silent world of mine, where nothing made sense and those around me were confused by this new me. I could see it in their eyes. They were feeling their own level of pain and loss. But I also realized that they were feeling hopeful, for they knew that I was a fighter and I would do all I could to regain as much of the old me as possible.

Many times we are simply bystanders to a life we cannot call our own. The yin and yang of this life are not always ours to control.

Spending time with friends was a good diversion, yet, as mentioned before, I could see in their eyes that they knew I was different. They were very honest with me. When I repeated myself and asked if I had, they responded with a very kind "yes." When I had memory issues, they kindly helped me remember and they would wait patiently as it took me many moments to recall a thought or to get the words out of my mouth. They were loving and patient. Yet they were also sad. It was not easy for them to see me, their once strong friend, unable to complete some of the simplest of tasks, and I could see that pain in their eyes. The Celia of the past was gone. They and I both knew it, and none of us knew if she'd ever return.

I also dealt with the embarrassment of not remembering people I had once known and to this day I am greeted by people who seem to know me quite well, yet I have no earthly idea who they are. Sometimes I'll ask their name, explaining that I simply don't remember. Most the time I gamely go along with the conversation hoping that at some point my brain will fire up and I'll remember, but that rarely happens. I have forgotten so much and so many.

Perhaps the most painful part of all of this was when I finally began riding again. I could only ride for short periods of time, but still, I was riding again. None of those I rode with in the past asked to ride with me again. It's almost as if they were frightened to ride with me, the girl with the "brain injury." So I rode alone.

There was one woman, Karen Baker, who did choose to ride with me. On that day, my horse Broer went down. I called my vet and had him look Broer over, at which time he performed several tests. Wouldn't you know it, after reviewing the tests, the vet said Broer could no longer go on those long rides — the horse had an ulcer. The vet explained to me that Broer was simply too old, and the ulcer exacerbated his frailty. Two-hour rides could no longer be ours. We'd have to shorten it to 30-minute, low impact rides. Funny how Broer and I both met our retirement at the same time. That is where we are today, an easy 30-minute ride every few weeks. We are both a bit broke, we are both a bit injured, yet we both take much glory in those 30 minutes and yes, we still ride under the full moon as often as we can, he and I alone, just as we always have.

Being led through the trees by the light of the moon is truly a magical ride.

I was still bouncing back and forth between denial and reality. There were days I believed all would heal itself and I would somehow recover. The doctors must have gotten it all wrong. Surely, there would be a miracle, for I had seen plenty in my lifetime in my work with the Moonlight Fund. I was determined to go on writing grants for the fund, managing all the business and moving forward. I was fooling myself, and all that did was to put me further behind in my recovery. I'm very good at being foolish on any given day.

I also had a big event staring me in the face. I was soon to be awarded the Distinguished Citizen Medal by the Daughters of the American Revolution. I knew that I would not only have to attend the event, I would also be expected to speak. Randy knew of this award and had planned to be at my side, and that made it even more difficult. The thought of being without him was heart-wrenching.

As I entered the room, nearly 1,000 attendees were present. I made my way to the table with my wounded soldiers, a place I felt safe, and I sat down quickly and made small talk. Shortly after, I was asked to sit at the head table. I did as I was asked, but I felt lost and uncomfortable. I was anxious to get back to the table with my military members. I gave it 15 minutes, then I worked my way back to the table with my soldiers, but that did not last long. I was quickly re-escorted back to the head table. As they began to announce my award, a large screen began to roll photos of me and my life — they had vetted me well. It was heartbreaking — the first photos were of Randy and me, as were several more. I sat motionless, the pain in my heart palpable. I knew that I would soon be asked to step forward, accept the award and speak. Something came over me as I took the stage and looked down upon my military members seated there. I threw my notes to the side and I spoke from my heart and into the hearts of the thousand-plus people in that audience. I knew my military members had my back and I certainly knew that Randy was right by my side. I spoke of my years of experience caring for burn survivors and in those moments, I owned it, I was Celia Belt. If only for those twenty minutes, I felt it, I felt my confidence, my old self. I also felt like I was being held together with super glue. I thank God for those few moments of grandeur, for they gave me a glimmer of hope for the future.

Other than the DAR event, I had the good sense to cancel several speaking engagements. I lived between denial and confidence, never sure which to trust. My ranch became my prison, a pretty nice prison on any given day, yet a prison it was. One thing I was sure of — I was going to work as hard as I could with my therapists and doctors, and I was determined to reach the highest possible outcome with my health. I had no idea what the new me would be, but I was willing to trust that with hard work and good therapy, I could become close to what I was. One thing I did know, and that was that I would seek out the very best doctors, therapists and clinicians in the field and with their help, I would come damn close to becoming the woman I once was.

I had my first grandchild on the way, and I knew I was in no shape to hold that child, so I made that one of my goals, to hold my grandson.

Celia holding her grandson Remington

MORE BRICKS TO LAY

My daughter, Hillary, and Remington

In the summer of 2018, Social Security contacted me regarding my appointment with a psychologist in Kerrville that would assess my cognitive abilities and the damage done to my brain and inner ear by the accident. She informed me at the beginning of our meeting that the testing would take four to five hours. That in itself horrified me. How could I take tests for that long? It seemed an overwhelming task and I was terrified.

I took a deep breath. I was as determined as ever to take each test, do my best and see where this would lead. There was a part of me that knew I needed to qualify for disability and then there was the other part of me that was stubborn and was going to prove everyone wrong. As the testing began, I did my best to feel confidant and secure, then things went south. I was unable to complete many of the tests. Things that on any given day I should have been able to perform I was at a total loss to complete. I could feel myself becoming more and more frustrated and I was having seizures, which further complicated the testing process.

I already knew that due to my ruptured vestibular I could not read anything lying flat and asked that things be placed upright. She accommodated this as best she could, yet even with this modification I could not complete much of the testing.

Then, the worst of things happened. In a very kind voice, she told me I was reading backwards. I, of course thought...that's crazy.... I'm reading...and asked if I might try again....and once again...I was told I was reading backwards. From there we attempted several other tests. Many she simply stopped and in that same kind voice told me, "Celia, you can't do this test." I felt like a failure. These were simple, fundamental tests and I was failing, miserably failing. The four to five hours of testing became just two hours, and I left feeling broken.

If I was reading backwards, and could not complete many of these tests, such simple tests, how could I go on to run the Moonlight Fund? The mission of my life is to help burn survivors. To do so requires sixty to seventy hours of grant writing, fiscal management skills, and numerous public speaking engagements.

How...how was I going to go on? My heart was completely broken as we left that parking lot, my daughter, Hillary, driving me home. I know she must have felt the complete sadness I felt in my heart. I was silent and broken. Yet, I also knew that without the help offered by disability I would be in a world of hurt. How would I be able to support myself, in my condition? I had to swallow deep and accept the fact that I needed help, not only from family and friends, but from the government, something I never imagined I would do in my lifetime.

My mind was reeling on the way home. Although I was determined to get better and run the Moonlight Fund, the practical side of me knew I would need help to keep the fund up to speed. I knew in my heart I had lost the skill set to do this work on my own, and once home I began making calls to my best volunteers and board members asking them to step up and take on more responsibilities. Together, we could do this, we could make sure the fund continued, I was sure of that. I needed help. I knew it and they knew it. Together we could implement a pivotal turn in operating the fund or it would be lost. I could not fathom that the largest and most giving nonprofit in the U.S. for burn survivors could simply go down due to one woman's brain injury. We are bigger than that and we have so many people to care for.

The Moonlight Fund was founded in 1998. The name came about when I was driving down the road thinking about one of my horses, Northern Moonlight. It occurred to me that a nonprofit for burn survivors should be "safe" — confidences should always be held in private and our clients should feel free to contact us with any need and feel safe sharing those needs. You may never see a burn survivor even though thousands live among you. That's because they isolate, they haunt the 24-hour Walmarts where they are safe from the harmful rays of the sun and the prying eyes of others. So we named our organization something "safe," Moonlight, and we are committed to keeping it and our clients safe.

Twenty-two years and 12,000 people later, this work needed to continue, with or without me. I might be the co-founder, but now I had to realize I was not the future. The future needed to be passed on to those as passionate about this mission as I was.

With the new information from my testing, I began scanning the internet for a program that could transpose my writing. I had to be able to help type grants for the fund and submit them properly.

I had purposely remained silent about my accident for quite some time. After so many years of my heading up the Moonlight Fund, if our donors were to catch wind that the founder/director of the fund had a traumatic brain injury, they might certainly rethink their giving and I could not risk that. I found a backwards text generator and we began writing all our grants using that. It was another six months before I taught myself to write and read correctly.

Amazingly, every single grant we wrote that year was approved. It was during this time that I also made the decision, with the help of friends, to complete my book *Remarkably Intact*. It had been in the works for several years and after the heartbreak of my accident, losing my baby sister and my husband, I wasn't sure which way to turn, so I turned north and finished the book, releasing it in September of 2018.

The book went on to be chosen as the best biography at the IndieReader Discovery Awards in June of 2019. I sent my friend Leigh Ann Kenney to New York to collect the award — my daughter was set to deliver her first child and that I could not miss. I am so glad that I stayed behind. Hillary had a traumatizing delivery and a C-section. We nearly lost both her and the baby. Remington is the joy of my life and his presence in my life helps ease the pain of not seeing my elder grandson, Korben.

I will never forget the moment when Leigh Ann rang me from New York. I was at the hospital about to enter my daughter's room. There were three books competing for best biography. I had thought I'd be lucky to be chosen third or possibly second. I was incredibly surprised when Leigh Ann informed me that *Remarkably Intact* had taken first place. I like to think my husband, looking down from the heavens, was helping me all along — he must have had something to do with that award. How a book about one burn survivor who helped thousands of others could be chosen as the number one biography was beyond me, yet it was. Thanks, Randy. Love you, buddy.

I believe that with all injuries, even brain injuries, we have the ability to retrain our bodies or minds, at least to some extent. To learn new ways of doing things, to regain our thought processes and become as close to whole as we once were is not such a farfetched thought. I never gave up then and I'm still fighting today to regain as much cognitive and physical ability as I possibly can. Yet I'm also realistic and know my boundaries.

My neurologist and therapists have all mentioned that I am extremely high-functioning considering the severity of the accident, but they also remind me of my limitations. I appreciate such comments and they provide me a measure of hope. But I know I will never be the same and I must do my best to work with what I've got. I am a new me. Accepting that new me is a heartbreak, yet I must plow headlong into the future with what assets I have available to me. I must find the silver lining in this. Perhaps it's this book, or that next person I meet who is struggling with their own brain injury. I've always believed that in all tragedy there is a measure of hope and learning, or a gift to be given.

Riding Broer into the sunset

LONG AND ROCKY ROAD

Taboo, my love

Since Randy's passing, I was cared for by home health aides. Nurses, physical and occupational therapists and eventually cognitive speech therapists were at my home several days a week.

One of my biggest issues was the medications my doctors had prescribed. The nurses set up several different ways for me to take my meds, assuming it would make things easier for me and I would not goof up the process, yet invariably I would. I'd end up taking the wrong pills, too many of this one, not enough of that one, and eventually I'd become very ill and realize what I had done. I found myself in the hospital more than once due to this confusion. I worked for months with the nurses on this issue, but nothing seemed to work until they developed a very simple plan for me. They drew a picture, front and back, of each pill, with its name, on a lined sheet of paper, and to this day I can manage my drugs quite well. I still have the occasional "goof," but for the most part, I take my pills on schedule. I might also add that my local CVS pharmacy caught on to my dysfunction and stepped in to ensure I have the correct medications when I need them.

I long for the day when I am no longer a slave to these pills. Yet when I have this conversation with my neurologist, he continues to inform me that this is a lifelong injury, that the seizures will always be a part of my life and the ruptured vestibular will never repair itself. I am who I am and must accept this. I guess this is my version of getting old — it's just come earlier in life than I would have liked.

An amusing part of my injury is that I constantly lose things — keys, remotes, purses, you name it, I'll lose it. When I purchased my car I asked for three sets of keys. It took only a few short months before all were lost and I was not even driving! My friends were driving me to appointments in the car, but still I lost all those keys. I keep a post office box downtown. I love the look on the postman's face each time I approach the front desk and inquire about purchasing a key. He always greets me with a kindly look, saying, "Another one?" The fun part of this whole mess is when I do actually find something, I get a good laugh out of exactly where things show up. Some come with some sweet memories. Just the other day I found a set of keys I had lost at the post office. On the fob was my husband's handwriting. He had meticulously labeled and dated the key ring. It was inscribed "home" and the date was four days after my accident. He obviously knew back then that he needed to begin the process of getting me organized. It was just another example of how he still looked over me and cared for me, just as he had for so many years.

Early in this process, the suggestion was made that I either move to a full-care facility or have someone move in with me. As you might imagine, I was not about to do either. Even the suggestion felt like a slap in the face and a huge blow to my ego. I felt perfectly capable of caring for my ten acres and all the animals myself. I admit the place is not cared for as nicely or as well as before, but I do a pretty good job of keeping up. My friends have been a tremendous help to me and I love them for it.

I was also told I would never ride again, drive again, work again, pretty much do anything again. I will admit here I could not even hold down a regular job. One good seizure at work, a bout of vertigo, one bad fall, to say nothing of my lack of hearing and my memory loss, means I am not the best candidate for a day-to-day job. I'll have to remember the good old days, when I ran companies and could bark orders and collect fat checks, and be thankful for those days, for they are gone. I have accepted that I will never be that woman again and I am grateful that I once was that woman. In turn, I am grateful for the woman I am today, I can hold my grandson, spend time with friends and enjoy the sunsets. Life may be different, but it isn't all that bad. We must find the good, the silver lining in all. We are lost without finding the light in all the darkness.

I was convinced I could kick start my brain with cognitive therapy, but although I continued to yearn and plead for it, I was constantly told, "You're not ready." After being under the care of two different neurologists, I had finally made my way to the one neurologist who was renowned in our area and throughout the nation. Tough to get in to see, but I did not give up.

Dr. Anand Mehendale had been mentioned to me by several of my doctors and I set out to become his patient early in this process. It took several months, but once I became his patient, all things changed and the level of care I received was well worth the wait. I had already lost my driver's license, something I knew would happen. Doctors are required to report patients with seizure activity to the state medical board. At this point, I was dependent on the charity of friends and family to cart me to doctors' appointments, grocery shopping and everywhere else. It was a demeaning experience to lose my license, my freedom.

My ranch became my prison, yet, as with all things, I found the humor in it and kept pushing forward. When I finally became a patient of Dr. Mehendale, he quickly began the process of running multiple EEGs and checking the Keppra (anti-seizure drug) levels in my blood. I must admit that at this point I was not taking the recommended dose. I am a bit anti-drug and did not like being on so many meds. So, of course, the Keppra levels came back bad, painting a clear picture of my noncompliance. But what was worse were the EEGs. I remember meeting with Dr. Mehendale in his office. My friend Leigh Ann had driven me and was by my side. Dr. Mehendale has quite a humorous spirit and as we were joking about this or that, I asked, "How were my EEGs?" We had completed a one-day and a four-day and I was anxious to hear the results. He looked at us, paused a moment, and his answer was like a dagger through my heart. "Your EEGs were grossly disturbing," he said. From there we entered a large room and he proceeded to pull up my EEGs and show us the results.

The shock did not end there, as he then explained that the right front lobe of my brain was also "spiking" (indicating seizure activity). My response to this was "NO!" I'd continually been told that I had damage to the two left lobes. Every previous test had shown damage in those areas only. This could not be correct. I could not have damage to three lobes! It was almost more than my heart could bear.

Yet, I believed in this man's expertise. It was a sad day, to say the least, to find out that not two, but three lobes of my brain had significant damage. My mind was truly spinning at this point. I simply could not take it all in. I asked him if he thought I might be able to drive soon and he responded, "You will probably never be able to drive." I also asked him if I could begin cognitive therapy. His response was, "You're not ready." I'd been hearing "you're not ready" for nearly two years and frankly, I was sick of hearing it and I was anxious to get this show on the road. After a bit more conversation, I agreed to go on a higher dose of Keppra, and he added one more anti-seizure drug and another drug for me to take while experiencing seizures.

Dr. Mehendale scheduled my next EEGs and Keppra blood work for 2020. This concerned me because my United Health Care insurance benefits provided at no cost by my late husband's employer were due to end in December of 2019. After that I would be on Medicare and would be responsible for co-pays. I left that day with a silent broken heart. Nonetheless, I had a plan. I was going to do everything I could to move the date of the tests to 2019 and pass the next EEGs and the Keppra bloodwork. Despite the tough results I'd just seen on the screen, I was planning on winning this battle and at least receiving a limited driving license. In my mind, I had the best doctor and the best attitude. All I needed was my best army, my own little personal army that consisted of drug compliance, hard work with my therapists, and a little help from the gods to pass the next round of EEGs.

I began taking the prescribed dosage of Keppa. It was four times what I had been taking. I felt physically awful, yet I knew I had to take this amount to pass the next blood test and get my seizures under control.

As my next appointment with Dr. Mehendale approached, I practiced my appeal. My daughter's first child was due in June and she would need my help. And there were the insurance benefits that were ending in December. I needed him to move up the date for my tests. I needed to pass those tests to regain my driver's license. As I explained all of this to him, I was startled by his quick response. He agreed to a four-day and a one-day EEG and to have my blood levels drawn the next month.

I was elated, yet cautious. I don't have the type of seizures that are obvious — in fact, many times I don't even know when they are happening. I could only hope that the increased dosage of Keppra and the two additional seizure meds had things under control. When the time came for my EEGs I felt like a child at Christmas time. I was so hopeful and full of excitement. But during the time I was undergoing the four-day EEG, I had a bad fall, a side effect of the ruptured vestibular in my inner ear. Not only was it a bad fall, I landed on my head, directly on one of the electrodes that was fastened to my forehead. I could not believe my luck. I was certain that this fall would show up on the testing as something negative and I would perhaps not pass. I was a mess of anxiety. I logged the fall on the recorder and in the logbook they gave me to report all events and hoped for the best.

I was over the moon when just two days after having the EEG monitor removed Dr. Mehendale rang me to say I had passed all my EEGs, my seizures were under control, and he would be issuing a letter to the state medical board that I was cleared to drive. He didn't mention my Keppra levels and at the time I didn't think to ask. A few weeks later I received my Keppra results. The therapeutic range is 12-46, mine was 59. I was taking a toxic dose of Keppra and my dosage was decreased immediately. This would certainly explain why I had been feeling so physically awful for the past months. I was unable to wake in the mornings or stay awake much of the day, I rarely ate, and my body felt sick in a way that's tough to explain. It took several weeks after cutting the dosage to feel close to "normal."

I look forward to the day when I can take fewer meds, but for now I must remain compliant. I know the day is coming when my doctors and I will be having that talk. It may not go my way and I'm OK with that. Although I might want to cut back, decrease my meds, and feel more normal, that might not be the healthiest thing for me to do. I want the old Celia back and yes, frustration is normal. But with these types of injuries, we must trust our doctors and work within the system to obtain the best possible outcome for our health. I must learn to be compliant, less stubborn and more willing to listen.

This may all seem to be a sad story, much like that of the champion thoroughbred racehorse Seabiscuit. After a run of impressive victories, the horse ruptured a ligament in his left front leg. Many, including trainers and jockeys, predicted he would never race again. But he had the heart to keep running, as must I. Seabiscuit retired from the track in 1940 as racing's all-time leading money winner.

Celia with Ember the wolf

PROTECT AND BETRAY

"Home" and "safe," my two favorite words

My appointment with Social Security was both good and bad. I was awarded disability and was thankful for that. I was relieved to know I would have some form of income — not much, but it was something, praise God.

That feeling was short-lived when I asked for what period of time I would receive disability benefits. The response I received tore through my heart. I'd worked with plenty of patients applying for Social Security over the years. I knew that one year, three years, sometimes five or seven years of benefits were awarded. As the Social Security rep looked over the screen and the paperwork, he slowly looked toward me and said, "It's permanent." Hearing those words, to have someone say I was "permanently disabled," put a dagger through my heart.

The pain went even further than that as he went on to explain that due to the extent of my injuries, I would not be allowed to manage my own funds; my daughter would now be listed as my payee. It was all I could do to choke back the tears. My heart tore in two and as I sat there I realized the life that lay before me was not at all like the life I had lived before. I was now listed as unable. I was now...disabled... unable to manage my own finances. I was no longer Celia Belt, powerhouse businesswoman, philanthropist, public speaker, author, hunter. At that very moment I felt like no one. I had become no one. The drive home was a quiet one. I held back the sobs and looked about in a confused state. I was shattered, I was broken, I was not Celia...and I was silent.

In the first year following my accident, I was dealing with the deaths of my sister and my husband, undergoing therapy, trapped at home due to having no driver's license, and making some poor decisions. Some of these decisions were financial.

My eldest son was expecting his first child and just two weeks before the birth he came to me explaining what a tough situation they had with their landlord. I couldn't bear the thought of them bringing my grandson home to such turmoil, so I offered to purchase a home for him. The only things I asked of him were that he bring my grandson to see me every other week because I could not drive, and that he repay $85,000 of the $260,000 that I was putting up for the home. It was a heartbreak and a reality check when he repaid me only $50,000. But worse yet, in the first year of my grandson's life, I saw him only four times and have not seen him since.

Another thing I did that was foolish was that I continued to give money to the Moonlight Fund. I donated nearly $90,000 in the year following Randy's death. Foolish behavior for a woman with no income on permanent disability.

I share these stories because I'd like to stress the point that making large financial decisions the year following your accident is a foolish thing to do. I was a widow with little income making foolhardy decisions. I simply was not thinking straight. Whether it was the brain injury or the loss of two close family members, I did not have my head screwed on straight and I was making some very poor decisions that would affect the rest of my life. I needed to get my mind back on track, a new track, and I began the process of realizing that I had a set amount of money that would have to last me the rest of my life. Although, I might add, a part of me will always be happy to have helped my son, regardless of the outcome.

A few months later, my Moonlight Fund board president and board treasurer asked if they might come out for a visit. I agreed despite being both curious and cautious as to why they would make the hour-plus drive to my home. What exactly did they want to discuss? My friend Bethany had plans to come visit that weekend and I asked if she might come a bit early and sit in on this meeting. I wasn't feeling comfortable and I needed her support.

As we were seated in my living room, the two board members asked, "Why is Bethany here?" I found that odd as they both knew Bethany. The conversation quickly went from friendly to confrontational. They began to question my health and the amount of money I was personally donating to the fund. Their intentions were good — they were concerned about me, my health and the amount of money I was donating and they felt the best thing to do was to shut the fund down until I was, in their opinion, well enough to manage it better. At this point, I reminded them that every grant we had written had been awarded and that the fund was doing quite well.

The fury that rose up inside of me was palpable — shut down the fund? Stop helping people, discontinue the retreats, start saying no to burn survivors who depended on us day after day? It took all I had to remain calm, yet I was. I said no, the fund would continue. These burn survivors counted on us in so many ways and we could not simply stop caring for them.

No one was going to take the Moonlight Fund away from me or those we served, not anyone. I might have been in no shape to operate the fund, but that did not mean we could not find a way to carry it forward under the direction of others.

Both handed me their resignation letters, and I thanked them for their years of service. Quite honesty, they had already served beyond their term limits, as had most of my board. It was time to rework the board and this just brought that need into full view.

After they left, Bethany and I discussed what had just taken place and what would need to be done to carry the Moonlight Fund forward. I looked at her and asked if she might consider joining the board and acting as secretary. She agreed. I immediately got on the phone and filled every board position within twenty minutes with well-qualified and dedicated board members, and I have never looked back. The fund has continued and is thriving to this day.

Today our board consists of not only business leaders, former military members, accountants and medical professionals, but many who have experienced a burn injury in their own family. The Moonlight Fund carries on, caring for more people than ever before, and nearly every grant we write has been awarded. We have helped more than 12,000 people in our 22 years, an accomplishment not achieved by many nonprofits. We do all this with low overhead, high giving, and 24/7 support.

My husband, Randy, asked me to do only two things before he passed away. One request was, "Don't leave our land." He knew how much I loved working on the land. He also asked me to "never stop raising money" for those we serve at the Moonlight Fund. Two simple requests from the man I loved so dearly, and I know he is watching over me and helping me in everything I do. We all have angels.

Toranado, Broer and I cool off

LIFE REBORN

Broer and I and my Kimber 308

I continued my home health care recovery. Nurses paid visits three days a week, physical therapists two days a week, and an occupational therapist two days a week.

Eventually I convinced my doctor to order cognitive therapy. I was elated! Finally I could begin the process of putting this brain back on track. But as I began this portion of my therapy, it came with some surprises. I imagined it being some intense and rigorous brain work; instead, the therapist pulled out the simplest of exercises. I felt as if I were back in grade school, yet I realized that this work was needed. I found I did not know how to properly fill out a check, or how to count money. I was shocked. I had been spending the last year and a half walking through life barely functioning but I had had no idea of my deficits.

I yearned to learn more and do the best I could do. I had completed my book, written grants, accepted awards, run my household, cared for my animals and managed my ranch, yet now I was finding out that my brain was still not functioning on all gears. It was a shock.

But the new challenges excited me, and I truly adored my therapist. I developed a newfound confidence. Whether I was at the store counting change or assisting with the financials for a grant, I could sense the old me coming back. I had not realized that up until this point I was struggling. How I was able to assist writing grants with detailed budgets, much less pay my bills and keep my household running, is something I will never understand, yet I did it for all those months.

With my therapist's help I could now see things clearly and I felt so much more like the old Celia. After several months and much improvement, the fateful day came. My therapist looked at me after one of our sessions and said, "We're done; you're finished with your cognitive work." My heart sank. I asked, "Why? Isn't there more we can do? I have great insurance. Let's keep going, let's learn more." However, she was firm — we were done. I realized I had become attached to her visits and truly enjoyed the progress I had made, and I did not want it to end. But end it did. I had accomplished what we set out to do and I was now on my own. I felt a bit frightened, but I also felt empowered.

I also began to feel confident enough to begin driving the Ranger on the property. It felt good to spread seed, harrow and inspect the land as I had done for years. The ranch needed some work, and although my friends had been helping out, it was in need of more work to bring it up to my standards. But, Lord, it felt so good to be out on the land, the dogs in the Ranger with me, the soil being tilled below me. I love the land — it's food for my soul. Just as the sunsets sing the language of love, the land sings the language of contentment to this heart of mine.

I was also making progress in other areas, with the help of my friends and family. We continued to write grants. I began to take on some public speaking gigs and I was able more or less to keep up with the ranch and house. Then it happened. I started falling. Always to the left, and frequently. Thankfully I missed my head, yet I came close, on one occasion. When I found I simply could not get up my dog Taboo pushed himself under me and literally lifted me up. I'm grateful I had Taboo by my side. There was not much that dog could not do for me.

As you might imagine, this was becoming frightening. I lived alone and I did not want one of my children or a friend to find me on the floor at some point, unresponsive. I needed to seek help. The ringing in my ears had also increased to such a high pitch that it sometimes was all I could hear. I suspected something was acutely wrong and that it had to do with the ruptured vestibular in my ear. I made an appointment to see my ear surgeon, Dr. Symms, and sure enough, after some testing, he diagnosed inner ear migraines. I'd never heard of such a thing, and quite frankly I thought, "What else could be wrong with me?" He reminded me that I would always be at risk for falls to the left but with the addition of this condition that risk had increased exponentially. He put me on three new meds and within two weeks the falls had decreased. I still have the ringing in my ears, the balance issues and the vertigo, but I am so thankful that Dr. Symms diagnosed the cause of the falls and provided the appropriate protocol to decrease their frequency.

My accident not only injured three lobes of my brain but it also permanently ruptured the inner vestibular between my brain and my inner ear. As I've mentioned before, this led to hearing loss, balance issues, vertigo and sight problems. It's important to seek a full diagnosis when you have a head injury and to take all the steps necessary to treat the symptoms. I say this because some of the secondary symptoms can be as life-threatening as the original injury.

As my symptoms began to ease, I felt better able to take on a few public events, but only when accompanied by a trusted friend or two and with Taboo by my side. One such event, sponsored by a Moonlight Funds donor, Chive Charities, is the annual Chive Green Gala, held each November in Austin, Texas. I had missed it the previous year and this year my friends Leigh Ann and Bethany planned to accompany me. Of course, I'd also have Taboo by my side. I felt confident attending with this trio to look after me. I was excited, purchased a new gown, and hired my hair and makeup team to travel to Austin. I was certain that this was it! I was now ready to reenter the world. The three of us attended the pre-party and at 7 o'clock we headed over to the gala. By 8, I felt completely exhausted. I did not have the energy I once had had. I asked Bethany and Leigh Ann if they would mind escorting me back to the hotel.

Just recently one of my doctors had prescribed Seroquel to help me sleep. It's important for those with brain injuries to obtain an optimal amount of sleep and although I was already taking a heavy cocktail of sleep meds, I simply was not sleeping. I dreaded the nights. Often the sun was rising before I could fall asleep; it was tortuous. So my doctor added 200 mg of Seroquel to my long list of nightly meds.

Just the week before Bethany found me sleepwalking at my home. We simply laughed it off, not taking into account just how dangerous sleepwalking can be. So on this night in Austin, Leigh Ann and Bethany accompanied me back to our suite at the hotel, tucked me into bed, made sure I took all my meds and headed back to the gala. They felt confident that I was fine with Taboo by my side and had no reason to fear for my safety.

I have faint memories of that night and they terrify me to this day. It was raining and I was dressed in pajamas with pants. I can remember walking through a parking garage and looking down at Taboo. He was walking close to me on my left. I also remember walking down a street and looking down at my dirty, wet pajama pants. I can remember the faces of people walking towards me. I can also see the hallways of the hotel I was walking through. I remember feeling very real, primal, fear. Somehow, I don't know how, I made it back to the room. The next morning, I awoke and roused Leigh Ann and Bethany and told them what had happened. I looked at my pajama pants lying on the floor and they were filthy and wet up to the knees. How far and how long I had walked, I had no idea. I was frantic. Someone could have taken Taboo. That was my biggest fear, and yes, someone could have hurt me. I rang security at the hotel and asked if they had caught me on camera or if I had gone to the desk to ask for help. I wanted to put the pieces of the night together. Once home, I rang my doctor and immediately reduced the dosage of Seroquel. I'd rather deal with a few restless nights than put myself and my dog in danger.

Dealing with a brain injury and all the medications that come with it is a tricky thing. It is important to exercise caution and to educate yourself on what drugs you're taking, the possible interactions among those drugs, and your tolerance for each.

Randy and I shortly after arriving in Africa

86

THE SPANIARD

Gary and I at play

Back in 2016 I had met Gary Rodriquez. He was handling all the print work for the Moonlight Fund. I found it odd that he would travel all the way out to my ranch to have a simple document signed. Somewhere in my soul I knew he wanted to meet me in person and that there was more to his visit than my signing a document.

I was, after all, a public figure and he had probably seen countless photos of me. He probably had no idea that I was a married woman. When he arrived, I was working in the barn. We met and exchanged pleasantries and I signed the document. I could tell by the look in his eyes that he was smitten. Several conversations later, I casually mentioned my husband.

From that point on we became fast friends. I knew he felt more for me than friendship and I realized that was something I would have to handle with kid gloves. He always went the extra mile when it came to providing the best printed products to the fund and driving to my home to deliver materials or simply to grab a signature from me. There was definitely an attraction, yet it was one that was forbidden. My marriage and his Catholic faith stood firmly in the way of either of us doing anything inappropriate.

Years later, when I lost Randy, I felt close enough to Gary to invite him to Randy's memorial service and after party. At this time, he had moved on to an advertising company and I gave him a shot at our business. Although that was not the best fit for the Moonlight Fund and the business relationship did not work out, we remained friends.

It wasn't long before Gary became a part of my inner circle, joining us for Moonlight Fund events, spending days at the river, or attending dinner parties at my house followed by long nights on the back deck taking in the stunning landscape and sunsets with my pack of close friends. Due to my home being so rural, many of my friends often spent the night. I was aware that each night he occupied one of my guest rooms was a challenge for him because he truly wanted to be with me. I was not ready for that and he respected my position, yet the anxiety he felt was obvious. And I'll admit here that I was beginning to feel a stirring in my heart for this man. Feelings that had long been gone were reappearing and I could not deny that I was developing an attraction towards this tall Spaniard.

As time progressed and we reorganized the Moonlight Fund board of directors. I asked Gary to become the vice president of the board. He accepted and has done a stellar job of navigating the fund forward. He also made himself available to drive me to various places such as doctors' appointments, grocery shopping, and so on. And he was my "go to" for picking up Moonlight Fund donations. He was a great help to me and never asked for anything in return.

It was quite obvious to me that his attraction had not waned, and I kept him at arm's length. Randy had been gone seventeen months, and I was still in a continued state of grief. One night, after another great dinner party and some time on the back deck with friends, he asked two of my dearest friends, Bethany and Leigh Ann, out of my earshot, what they would think if he asked me out on a date. Their response was immediate and firm: "Celia's not ready." The three of us were close, and they knew all too well that I was still grieving for my husband as well as for my sister. The thought of another man in my life was the furthest thing from my mind.

But Gary was not ready to give up. He continued to spend as much time with me as was allowed, and with my friends and my family. He was becoming more of a permanent fixture in my life and he looked after me in a way others did not or could not. He watched over my health, kept track of my pills and my doctors' appointments and kept a very close eye on me during seizures or episodes of vertigo. Slowly, he was becoming my partner on many levels. I, on the other hand, had told myself that I would not consider dating until the two-year anniversary of Randy's passing, and I meant to stick to that.

As the date approached, I took a hard look at my life, I also looked at the lives of those around me. I watched intently as my friends interacted with their husbands, and a place in my soul longed for those bygone days. Dating might not be so bad. I knew Randy would not want me to be alone. Yet, I couldn't help but still feel a strong connection to Randy and a piece of me felt that I might be betraying his memory should I move forward with this relationship.

Nonetheless, I did so. On a chilly December evening in 2019, I built a fire and sat down with Gary, "my Spaniard." We had a long talk. I poured my heart out to him, explaining why I had rejected him for so long and what I felt I had to offer on a long-term basis. I also shared my feelings for him, feelings that I had kept hidden and tucked deep down inside of me.

Gary accepts me for who I am — a woman with a brain injury and a support dog, a woman overly dedicated to the

Moonlight Fund, a country-loving girl who rarely wears makeup and prefers her back deck to a night out. On that night we became handfast, as I call it, dedicated to one another and no other. On that night I knew I would no longer be alone. I now belonged to another and it felt good.

Although the relationship did not last, I am thankful for the time we spent together. The coronavirus hit and with that and many other issues, my life was about to change on many levels.

Soon after, I received word that I had been chosen as the Philanthropist of the Year by the Association of Fundraising Professionals. I was incredibly honored and as I took a look at who had won in the past, I felt completely out of my league. I've been blessed with several awards for my work over the years, yet, I always ask myself, why am I being awarded for something I was meant to do and love so much. I'm always incredibly humbled that others notice the work I do and it brings a new level of attention to the Moonlight Fund, now that's, something that really excites me! You see, even with a brain injury, you can still be honored and that's pretty special, on all levels.

Gary and I

AS I AM

My children, Justin, Jarred and Hillary

My wish to have my EEGs and blood Keppra levels done in 2019 was granted by Dr. Mehendale. So in August I underwent another series of EEGs and had my Keppra levels tested. My seizures were finally under control with these meds, according to the EEGs. I was elated to get the call from Dr. Mehendale that he would issue a letter saying that I was able to drive again, although he cautioned me as to how much driving I should do. No long distances or full days in the car.

I can't describe the sense of freedom this gave me, after two years of not driving. I could now drive downtown and pick up milk or dog food. Or should one of my animals have an emergency, I could now drive to the vet's. I'm fortunate to live in a small town. I can't imagine that I'll ever be driving into San Antonio or anyplace far away, yet here in my town I can pick up my mail and do my own grocery shopping. We take driving for granted, until we can't do it. Believe me...it's a luxury. Once it's gone, our home becomes our prison, and asking people for rides, well, it became humiliating for me.

I thought that driving again would be as simple as getting back on a horse. It was not. I suffered from great anxiety. I had plenty of horns honked at me, and I did make a few mistakes. Thank God they did not end up in accidents, although I came close on many an occasion. I learned quickly that my driving would have to be kept to very short trips and that I would have to be very cautious. I realized that this was not just due to the fact that I had not driven in two years. It was also due to my health. I never know when a bout of vertigo or a seizure will hit, so at every intersection I look several times, I drive slowly, I don't drive far and I never drive at night. Yet it is still a bit of freedom to drive into my small town and collect the mail or pick up some hay for the horses. It is a baby step that I am grateful for but I still know I have to be extremely careful.

My life today is not as it was before the accident. A brain injury requires more sleep than I was accustomed to, and sadly, my memory will never be the same. I know full well there are memories that are lost to me, perhaps forever. But the funny thing is, if you don't have the memory, you don't know what you're missing, so I get a laugh out of that. I have developed coping skills for many things in my life. Some work, others don't.

Perhaps the most awkward thing is not remembering people. I recognize their faces and I certainly know that I know them, yet there is no name I can put to the face and no memories of our time together. I find myself simply staring into their faces, engaging in idle conversation and having no clue who they are. I must fake it till I make it in most circumstances.

Although I am a very private person, because I live in a small town most people know of my accident. They may not know all the details, but they know I suffered a brain injury and have not been out and about much since. I'm sure the gossip has run high and low and that most people don't know the true details of what I've gone through, and that's OK with me. The mountain I have had to climb would be difficult for most of them to fathom. This accident did not change the fact that I am a private person; it simply increased it.

I've accepted the fact that I will probably never be able to hold a "real" job. I'll never be that powerhouse woman who ran companies, collected a big salary and enjoyed life on a large scale. Yet, I know that with the help of others I can still complete grants for the Moonlight Fund that are compelling and on target. That's the "miracle" piece of things for me, that I can still produce compelling grants that are awarded and make it possible for the Moonlight Fund to carry on. That piece of me remains at full strength. The love I bear for the fund is so engrained in my mind, it's a miraculous thing to have lost so much of my mind, yet this piece remains.

I recently started riding my horse again, but our excursions are different from before the accident. Broer is getting old and is now retired; his condition fits this body and mind of mine perfectly. We've been together off and on since 2004, and now as we enter this retired portion of our lives, we are perfectly suited to one another. As I ride him, visions and thoughts of our days of grandeur fill my head. I can almost feel my body moving in all those upper-level dressage moves, even though we are simply enjoying the cadence of a simple, peaceful walk together. I wonder if he is thinking of those days also.

There are many days that my heart breaks for the things I once enjoyed — skydiving, skiing, dressage riding, working out. Heck, just being awake for most of the day. But those days are gone, and I can only hope to regain them little by little or to be realistic and know that most of that life will never come my way again. Acceptance is a big word. It takes strength and backbone to accept things in life, the good and the bad.

I do drive now, although it's just short trips into my small town. I'm not ready to drive into a big town or for a long distance, and I don't know if I ever will. I should have died on that fateful day and nearly did. It was a bad injury, one that many do not survive. Many times, I felt robbed. That should have been my Valhalla. I should have gone off the back of a horse. Yet, there was work for me to do here. My sister needed me to be here for her to cross over, as did my husband. There will also be burn survivors who need the help of the Moonlight Fund. I now have two grandsons whom I hope to inspire to be the best versions of themselves. They will never know the Mimi that I could have been, but I'm doing all I can to be the best Mimi I can be today.

This life of mine has been full of so many experiences. You can refer to them as good or bad, but they are just experiences. Much like the stars in the sky, many shine bright while others simply cast light. My childhood traumas made me strong and this injury has made me different, and yes, perhaps a bit stronger in an odd sort of way. I will always struggle with seizures, memory issues, balance, vertigo and vision problems and all that comes with an injury such as mine. Yet I can still laugh with friends, hug my loved ones and spend time with my beloved animals.

Life is not fair, but it is just. Each of us will have our highs and our lows. The yin and yang of this life balances out in the end, and all we can do is accept the lot we have been given and look to the next life for what adventures await us there.

Over the years, through my work with the Moonlight Fund, I've met many people who are angry with their injuries. Several, sadly, have committed suicide. I am not here to judge and say that was a bad choice for them, although I wish they had chosen otherwise. I wish I could have helped them see that there is so much more to life than the tough cards they have been dealt. I cannot say there were not days that I wished it would all end for me, but in the end, the love I have for my charitable work, my friends, my family and my animals pulled me through the worst times. I was somehow able to remain focused on the light, even on the darkest of days.

Recovery is possible — perhaps not a full recovery, but enough recovery for you to enjoy a full and meaningful life. For those of you without insurance, there are resources available to provide the rehabilitative care you need to get back on your feet. Don't give up and let the system label you as "disabled." Find your own label, find your name, your course and your destiny. Strive to be the best version of yourself and hold on to the pieces of your life you cherish the most.

A part of me will always long for my old life. My daily struggles will always present problems. But I must live with them and know that I was blessed to survive that fall and work through my struggles to be the woman I am today. I have learned to enjoy the sunsets, my friends, my beloved family and the continuing work done by the Moonlight Fund. I can hold my grandchildren, a blessed thing indeed. I have learned to live with the disdain with which many people treat me because I know, as I hope they never do, what it is to deal with a brain injury. I am sad for my losses and happy for my gains and I have hope for the future. For, whatever that future may be, it is mine.

It is the silent warrior in all of us that gives us the strength, to live through life's greatest tragedies.

Sunset with Broer

RESOURCES FOR THOSE SEEKING HELP

www.biausa.org

www.medicinenet.com/ruptured_perforated_eardrum/
article.htm

www.caregiver.org/traumatic-brain-injury

www.neuroskills.com/patients-and-families/family-resources/

https://msktc.org/sites/default/files/
TBIFactsheetBookletEnglish508.pdf

AUTHOR BIOGRAPHIES

Celia Belt, Co-Founder of Moonlight Fund, Inc.

Celia Belt is the founder of the award-winning Moonlight Fund Inc., a 501(c)(3) nonprofit organization that provides financial, emotional and in-kind assistance to burn and blast survivors and their families. A burn survivor herself, Celia noticed the need for care and support for burn survivors throughout the country, and, along with Henry Coffeen III, she started the charity in 1998 in San Antonio, Texas. Since then, the organization has helped nearly 12,000 people across the U.S.

Celia has served as a public speaker for the Moonlight Fund and other organizations. In 2012, she was invited to speak at the Pentagon on behalf of the Moonlight Fund when the charity was named the top nonprofit in the country and given the Fisher House/Newman's Own® Award. In her audience were key military members, including General Martin E. Dempsey and Admiral James A. Winnefeld, Jr. Celia continues to speak on several subjects related to the needs of burn survivors, and on topics such as nonprofit management, overcoming childhood trauma and women's empowerment.

Celia and the Moonlight Fund have received numerous awards. In addition to the Moonlight Fund being named the top nonprofit in the country, Celia was awarded the *San Antonio Business Journal*'s Woman in Leadership Award and was chosen as a mentor, three years running, for the *Business Journal*'s Mentoring Monday. Celia was presented with the Distinguished Citizen Medal by the Daughters of the American Revolution (DAR), and most recently, she was presented with the Association of Fundraising Professionals' Outstanding Philanthropist Award.

Originally from Rockford, Illinois, and now a Bandera, Texas resident, Celia has published various articles in prominent publications including *San Antonio Medical Magazine, Dallas Safari Club, The New York Times, San Diego Magazine.* Her first book, *Remarkably Intact: Angels are No Strangers to Chains,* launched in 2018. It has received multiple outstanding reviews and was chosen as the best biography at the IndieReader Discovery Awards in 2019. She donates all book and public speaking proceeds to the Moonlight Fund.

Bethany Coomes, Author

Bethany was born and raised in San Pedro, California. She served in the United States Army as a mental health specialist. She currently resides in Cibilo, Texas with her husband Clayton, a retired military nurse. Clayton served on the burn unit at Brooke Army Medical Center during the war years 2008-2011. Bethany's daughter, Stella, suffered a burn injury in 2016 and has recovered well. She's an active mother, raising three children and donating time to local charities, including the Moonlight Fund. Bethany is also on the board of the Moonlight Fund and holds the position of Secretary.

MOONLIGHT FUND

Flashpoint!

It happens in an instant. A bomb detonates, a pan of grease spills, gasoline ignites. Fire consumes anything and anyone it its path.

Devastation

The average length of a hospital stay for a burn survivor is 93 days. However, depending on the severity of injuries, and the physical and occupational therapy a survivor requires, it can take years for life to return to some level of normalcy. Burns are life-changing injuries. In addition to the physical suffering, many times homes and personal belongings are destroyed by the fire. Extended medical treatments can mean lost jobs. To make matters worse, many burn patients are uninsured or on government assistance, putting them In a devastating financial situation just at the time when physical therapy or psychological counseling are most needed.

The Needs Were Great. The Support Was Not.

The number of burn survivors in this country is astronomical. Their emotional and financial needs can be staggering. Moonlight Fund was established because there was not enough support for the survivor or their families. It is our goal to provide whatever we can to make life better for these people.

Finding the New Normal

The instant someone becomes a burn survivor their life and the lives of their family and friends change forever. The Moonlight Fund provides 24/7 assistance to burn survivors and their family members, as well as families who have lost a loved one to a burn injury. Moonlight Fund addresses survivors' financial, emotional and physical concerns in the hour of need. Moonlight Fund is a 501(c)(3) non-profit organization. The fund is a GuideStar Platinum Participant.

We Measure our Success by the Lives We Touch

Moonlight Fund has helped nearly 12,000 burn survivors and their family members. It is the only organization of its kind, offering services from onset of an injury, through rehab and on into the patient's and families' new lives. The organization helps military and civilian survivors in many ways, including paying medical bills, providing financial aid to finish college degrees, building and furnishing homes, and most importantly, providing a support system when it is most desperately needed. The proceeds from this book will be donated to the Moonlight Fund to further help burn survivors.

We Operate Lean So We Can Help More

The majority of funds raised support programs specifically designed to meet the needs of burn survivors. We purposely maintain minimal operation costs. Today, you'll find Moonlight Fund assisting with everything from wound care supplies, education costs, rehab, counseling, and building of ramps and furnishing homes. These are just a few of the things the fund offers. Original co-founder Celia Belt continues to dedicate her time to the fund. She is supported in her efforts by an active and caring board of directors, volunteers, and a dedicated administration staff.

Programs

Financial Aid

Moonlight Fund actively raises money throughout the year in an effort to support those with financial needs (such as gaps in medical care, rehabilitation services, burial expenses, housing, and transportation). Additional services include child care assistance, tuition expenses, and referrals to third-party support services. The Fund is open to any request. We do ask that all requests be made in writing by the attending physician, case worker, or qualified rehabilitation or educational facility.

Retreats for Burn Survivors and Their Families

Moonlight Fund retreats are held several times a year at Silver Spur Ranch in Bandera, Texas, nestled in the beautiful Texas Hill Country. These 4-day gatherings offer an opportunity for those with recent injuries to spend time with fellow long-term survivors. The retreat provides alternative healing modalities (massage, Reiki, yoga, and healing studio sessions), and emotional support to both patient and family members. The weekend is low key, a relaxed temporary escape from the medical world. It's a traditional dude ranch experience with horseback riding and true Western culture. Retreats are open to all who have suffered a burn injury.

Emotional and Informational Assistance to Patients and Families

Moonlight Fund provides 24/7 access to emotional, financial, and in-kind services. In an effort to provide hope and peace of mind, it's important for those we serve to know they are not alone in this struggle. Our presence on burn units and in rehabilitation facilities is a large piece of what we do. We also are very active in the area of negotiating the costs of ongoing treatment, funeral services, housing, and child care. As part of our commitment to the healing process, we host monthly social groups. Moonlight Fund works with like-minded organizations to secure additional assistance for those we serve.

Home Sweet Home

Moonlight Fund offer home modifications to handicapped and wheelchair-bound burn survivors. Kitchen and bath renovations, ramps, and lowering of cabinets are just a few of the services we provide. With our corporate sponsors and retail partners, volunteer assistance and discounts from local contractors, we now have the capacity to help long after the patient and his family leave their medical environment.

Solicitation and Distribution of In-Kind Goods

This service is provided to those who may have lost household goods due to their accident, (such as clothing, computers, furnishings, household goods and automobiles). We also distribute wound care supplies, and physical therapy equipment to those who cannot afford them following their accident.

Caregiver Assistance

Being a caregiver for someone who has been burned requires empathy and patience. The abilities of the survivor have changed in an instant and depending on the severity of the burns, their independence can be gone for years. The caregiver usually takes on greater responsibility for the family's well-being. Moonlight Fund is there to help. We have volunteers who can help with the tasks you can't get to because your attention is where it should be – with your loved one. We also teach caregivers how to take on many of the medical responsibilities the survivor's injuries require.

Social Groups

For a burn survivor the physical pain can be severe, but the anxiety, fear, and emotional torture the injury causes can be even more debilitating. The accident also affects the people who are part of the survivor's life.

We make sure neither group is alone. We surround them with other survivors, people who have gone through this part of Hell and survived. We can help, with caring people to share the journey and resources to make burn recovery easier. Monthly social groups include activities such as bowling, indoor skydiving, pool parties and movies.

Beginnings

Moonlight Fund Inc. was founded in 1998 in San Antonio, Texas, by Celia Belt, fellow burn survivor Henry Coffeen III, the family of Ben Jones, the staff at the Burn Unit at the San Antonio Military Medical Center (SAMMC), and executives at Ernst & Young.

Founders

Celia Belt, Founder

"My mission is to let fellow burn survivors know they are not alone," says Celia. "I want to offer a hug, a smile, and a heart that cares. It is crucial to educate the public about the needs of burn survivors and their families as well as the lack of services available to them. We are here to care for burn survivors, their families and those who have lost a loved one to a burn injury."

Henry F. Coffeen III, Co-Founder

"On a sunny November afternoon, I finished my pre-flight inspection and hopped into the cockpit of my custom-built EDGE 450 aerobatics monoplane. The sky had never seemed bluer, the hum of the engine as I took off, never sweeter. I headed into an upside-down half outside loop with a two-point roll followed by a snap roll. Sheer exhilaration surged through me as I shot skyward. What was that? A damp and acrid fluid soaked my arms and chest. Fuel! Ruptured fuel tank! As I righted the plane, the cockpit filled with flames.

"Beating at my burning clothes with one hand, I switched off fuel, mags, master switch, and dropped into a nosedive. If the wind doesn't put this out fast I'll be too low to jump! Plunging, I opened the canopy and released the seat belts. Groping for the D-ring on my parachute, I ejected at 400 feet. Where's that ring? The Velcro that should have held it to my chest had burned away. I was free-falling. Then my fingers closed on the ripcord. I yanked it and felt my body hoisted upward. The ground quickly closed in, knocking the wind out of me. I tugged off the melted mass that had been my goggles and looked down. The fire was out, but my arms were absolutely white. I'm burned bad. My lovely plane was a smoking tangle of metal. I wrestled out of my chute and started walking. I walked the whole way to the airfield, three-quarters of a mile, before the pain began. I remember the helicopter trip, being wheeled into the burn unit at Brooke Army Medical Center. The medical team cut away what was left of my clothes. Then a mask closed over my nose and mouth and I sank into blackness. That first pain-racked week at B.A.M.C. burn unit was a battle simply for survival. Once I was stabilized, the grafting began, using unburned skin from my back, thighs, and scalp. During two lengthy operations the grafts were secured with more than 3,000 staples through my flesh. Here I was, the self-made guy, lying helpless in a hospital bed. How much more torture could I endure?

"The physical therapy to stretch the healing skin was agony, but the worst was the scrub baths – two a day. The nurses were merciless in their mission to rub every inch of my flesh raw. No screaming or pleading would sway them, and as the hour approached I'd actually cry in dread. Gritting my teeth as the brutal brush scoured away, I'd think, I don't even have say-so over my own skin. The nurse lifted me back onto my bed. Each touch, even the breeze he stirred as he left, brought tears to my eyes. After a month in the hospital I was released to continue my recovery. With me came a whole new orientation. Physical and occupational therapies were grueling and I, the self-reliant guy, was learning another kind of reliance.

"Today I can hide the scarring except on my hands. I'm not sorry it shows. It's a reminder of other hands with scars on them.

Henry currently lives in the Fort Worth area with his wife Trish and their five children. He stays busy running multiple companies including: Coffeen Management – Automotive Consulting; Jet Link – Aircraft Management; Lone Star Yamaha; and GI Tax – Tax Service. Henry has returned to his love of flying and pilots his personal jet for business and pleasure. Henry's legacy of giving to those less fortunate is a founding principle of Moonlight Fund.

The Family of Ben Jones

On July 28, 2000, Benjamin Scott Jones was injured in a car accident in Caldwell, Texas. He suffered burns over 45% of his body and was air-lifted to Brooke Army Medical Center in San Antonio. He lived on the Burn Unit in critical condition for 36 days. On September 1, 2000, he passed away from pneumonia. Ben was 22 years old, a student at the University of Houston and a decorated ROTC Cadet in the University of Houston Cougar Battalion.

Moonlight Fund's founding efforts were assisted by Ben's parents, Scott & Doris Jones, and uncle, Chuck Jones. We are grateful to them for their support of Moonlight Fund.

Moonlight Fund Stories

Ivan

As fate would have it, Ivan took over for the regular driver that day in Afghanistan. The Insurgents were patient and set off the IED when it would do the most damage – as the bus carrying 17 soldiers rolled over it. The bus was tossed and caught fire. Ivan hung upside down by his seatbelt. There was only one way out – over 16 dead soldiers. This fight to the back of the bus choked him. As he stumbled out, the bus exploded. Even though he was in a convoy, he waited for thirty minutes until his group found him. He was presumed long gone. He proves them wrong even today.

Javier

When a United States Army General flies in to see how a communications station is working and needs a driver, he gets one. Javier drew that assignment on that November day in Afghanistan. With his infectious smile he, his best friend, and the general loaded up and headed through the pass. There was one way in and one way out, with a choke point along the way. The first vehicle missed the pressure plate. Javier's did not. The explosion left Javier badly burned and the other two dead. He still has a smile, because not even the Fires of Hell can take that from him.

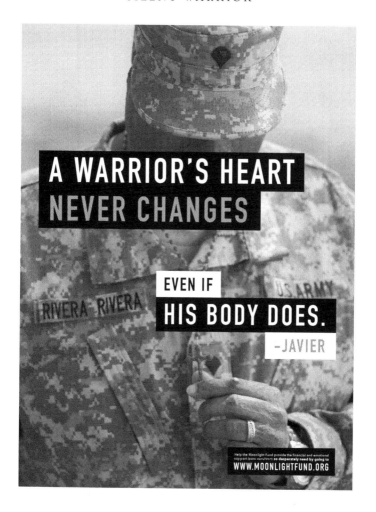

A WARRIOR'S HEART
NEVER CHANGES

EVEN IF
HIS BODY DOES.
-JAVIER

Help the Moonlight Fund provide the financial and emotional
support burn survivors so desperately need by going to
WWW.MOONLIGHTFUND.ORG

Misty

With their mother pulling a late night shift, Misty's older brother was left as the man in charge. The oil in the pan flashed and caught fire. The two reacted as a team — with his bare hands her brother grabbed the pan, while Misty headed through the smoke to save the dog and open the front door. Fate isn't always fair. The pan was searing as he headed from the kitchen, the dog stepped the wrong way and tripped Misty and her brother. The oil and gravity did the rest, with a beautiful young girl in its path. Misty is proof that a woman is not defined by the length of her hair but by the struggles she's overcome.

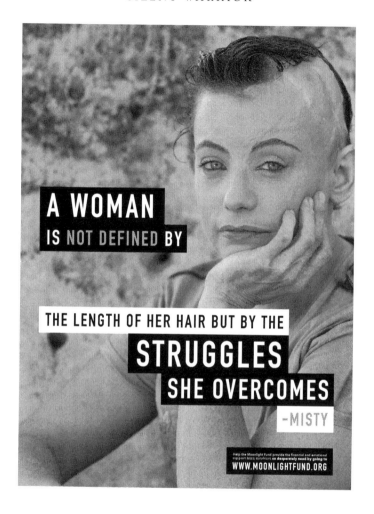

A WOMAN IS NOT DEFINED BY THE LENGTH OF HER HAIR BUT BY THE STRUGGLES SHE OVERCOMES

-MISTY

Help the Moonlight Fund provide the financial and emotional support burn survivors so desperately need by going to
WWW.MOONLIGHTFUND.ORG

Alex

As the eldest son in a Samoan village, Alex's destiny was to be the Manaia, or Chief. However, he gave that honor to his younger brother in order to enlist and fulfill an even greater calling. In the process he exchanged one legacy for another. The first explosion came and took its toll. So did the next two, each on different tours. His deployments as an Army gunner resulted in Alex being blown up not once, but three times. Obviously, "The third time's a charm" doesn't apply to a man who refuses to break.

Shilo

Routine was rarely routine in southern Iraq. As the Humvees slowly followed each other, keeping their staggered distance, it happened. The air was suddenly sucked out of the cab. Flames shot out of air vents. The vehicle erupted, tires and bodies blew skyward, gasoline and ammunition ignited. Shilo battled to get clear of the exploding wreckage as his body began to char. He was instinctively shouting orders while his body armor melted into his skin. What Shilo would learn over the next years and 60-plus surgeries was that flames can transform you into something even better.

Mario

Being engulfed in flames was just the painful beginning. Losing a limb stole another piece of who Mario was. But lying on the table, heart not pumping, legally dead, that's where it all started to unravel. Mario remembers sitting in Hell talking to demons before the doctors revived him. After that, Mario's life became a blur of pain killers, alcohol and days of complete self-absorption. His life became a medicated memory, until one night he overdosed. He flat-lined, but this time when he came back he chose another path and dedicated himself to live in the light. Fire forges steel. The Fires of Hell can forge a man's destiny.

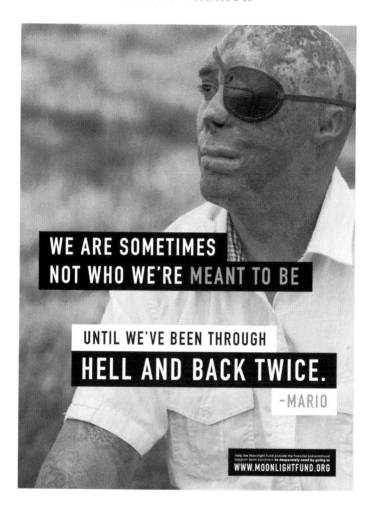

WE ARE SOMETIMES
NOT WHO WE'RE MEANT TO BE

UNTIL WE'VE BEEN THROUGH
HELL AND BACK TWICE.

-MARIO

Help the Moonlight Fund provide the financial and emotional
support burn survivors so desperately need by going to
WWW.MOONLIGHTFUND.ORG

Moonlight Fund Partners

Chive Charities, Tito's Handmade Vodka, U.S. Trust, Enterprise, HEB, Citibank, San Antonio Area Foundation, Genevieve and Ward Orsinger Foundation, Servant's Heart Foundation, The ASMBA STAR Foundation, Catrina's Ranch Interiors, Carl C. Anderson Sr. & Marie Jo Anderson Charitable Foundation, Earl C. Sams Foundation, Disabled American Veterans Charitable Service Trust, Newman's Own, The Home Depot Foundation, KCI Servant's Heart Foundation, The Perry & Ruby Stevens Charitable Foundation, South Texas Hispanic Fund, On the Move, Inc., and Airpower Foundation.

Moonlight Fund Bandera Office

P.O. Box 1299 Bandera, TX 78003

info@moonlightfund.org

Moonlightfund.org

ALSO BY CELIA BELT

Remarkably Intact

Winner, Best Biography, Indie Reader Discovery Book Awards, 2019—a truly remarkable accomplishment for a first-time author.

"Remarkably Intact is an inspiring and positive story of one woman not only surviving, but learning to thrive despite everything life could throw at her."

— Catherine Langrehr for *IndieReader*

Everyone has a story to tell. Some stories, however, serve a higher purpose: teaching people how to rise above the challenges in the road of life and achieve dreams that they once thought were impossible.

Celia Belt's *Remarkably Intact* is just such a story. It's a true tale of survival, strength, and sacrifice. It is a story of a woman who refused to let her physical and emotional injuries dictate her life. This unexpected guide to life is a blueprint drawn from Celia's own incredible struggles as a burn survivor, business professional, charity leader, author, and public speaker. Throughout the book, Celia candidly shares her "can-do" attitude and ideology for overcoming the odds. Anyone facing daunting hurdles will find *Remarkably Intact* an indispensable companion and source of heartfelt inspiration.